It's not a boy!

By
Vicky Turrell

Published by Leaf by Leaf Press Ltd 2017
www.leafbyleafpress.com

ISBN 978-0-9957154-2-4

Printed and bound by Clays Ltd, St Ives plc

For Tom.

Acknowledgements

I would like to thank members of Oswestry Writers Group for their encouragement and members of Leaf by Leaf Press for all their support and help.

I would also like to thank John Heap for arranging my story to enable printing and Kirstie Edwards for her cover painting.

My thanks go to Helen Baggott for her expert editing and to Georgina Aldridge from Clays for her help and guidance in their printing process.

I am indebted to my parents who worked hard all their lives and encouraged me in my career. Their cousin Harry Watson (1871 – 1936) inspired me, from childhood, with his paintings.

Lastly, a special thanks to my husband, Reg Turrell, who has patiently endured many hours listening to extracts from my story.

It's not a boy!

By
Vicky Turrell

Posty.
Reg Turrell

Chapter 1

Victorious Day

"Not long now," they said. "Don't give up, you can do it, there's light at the end of the tunnel." But the pain had seemed to go on forever and Mam said it was hard to believe it would end. Then suddenly it did. They had laboured and hoped for this. And then in the morning there was peace.

World War Two was over and to the sound of cheering, my mother's labours had also finished and I was born with my very own war about to begin.

I didn't know anything of the darkness that had just gone, but they told me later.

I didn't know about the first bomb that dropped in our paddock leaving a black, burnt, hollow tree. I never saw the soldiers making a concrete base for their guns in our field called Far Side. I didn't know about the air raid shelter that was made with straw bales – I never had to run there when the warning sounded. I didn't hear the man on his bike, with his old-fashioned dripping carbide lamp, pedalling furiously from Ringam to our village shouting,

"They're out – they're out!" And that meant that enemy bomber aeroplanes were out to get everybody.

Those were black days but that morning I slithered out into a victorious day – the darkness had gone at last and I blinked into bright welcoming light. I was in my mam's arms in my Aunty Martha's bed at her house at Ringam and I was safe.

"She's out, she's out." The news would go round the village but it was not shouted by our man on his bike because I found out later that he only liked bad news.

My two little sisters, Katy and Gwendy, climbed the stairs and came in to see me. So, there we all were, Mam and her three little daughters.

Aunty Martha sat on the edge of her bed with my mam and listened to their wireless. "Today is Victory in Europe Day." Everybody had worked so hard to bring victory and lots of people like Aunty Martha had prayed hard as well. They all cheered and Mam named me Victoria. I was named after a victorious day.

We stayed at Aunty Martha's for two weeks but my dad didn't have much time to come and see us because he was always busy working on our farm and looking after our animals. 'God helps them that help themselves' was one of his sayings and he believed it. My Aunty Martha believed in prayer but Dad believed in hard labour. Our farm was our livelihood and now he had another little girl to look after he had to work even harder.

Nothing was ever said of course, but my dad must have wanted his third baby to be a boy – you just knew that he would have wanted me to be a boy. He was a farmer and he had a farm to look after and he needed a boy to work with him and then take over from him when he got too old. Now he had three girls and no boy to help, so you could say that a second sort of bomb had dropped with my birth even though the war had ended. There was no boy – no son for my dad, third time baby not lucky.

Mam told me that when I was two weeks old, in between feeding his sheep and sorting his lambs for market, my dad came to pick me up in our little black car. My mam sat in front with me snuggled against her, wrapped in a grey army blanket. My sisters sat in the back and we chugged from Ringam to our own little village called Gumbalding – Gum for short. We went down our lane and I was carried into our house for the first time.

There was a fire roaring in the grate and I was put down on our horsehair couch to stare at the bright flames. Grandma from next door came to see me and she put the kettle on. Then they all sat down for a mug of tea. This was my home – this was where my mam thought that she would look after me. This was where I would be safe and where I would grow up.

I soon fitted in to my mam and dad's routine and it was as if I had always been there. Mam and Dad got up early and my mam lit the fire as she always did. Dad had a mug of tea then went out to look after his animals on our farm as he always did. Then our Katy went on a bus to school and Gwendy stayed with me and played. Everything went on as it always had and everything seemed safe. But it was not safe because, believe it or not, a third sort of bomb dropped on our family. This one was worse than the one that killed a tree and even worse than me not being a boy.

I can't remember anything about all this of course but this is what they told me. When I started to cut my teeth, I got fretful and grizzly and Mam rubbed some teething powder on my red gums and I settled down again. That was when this third bomb dropped.

Third time was not lucky again because something very dangerous happened to me but nobody knew what it was.

Something was wrong with me and I lay on our hard couch in pain staring unseeingly and everybody tiptoed past. Nobody knew what to do. My arms and legs stopped working, I couldn't kick about like I used to and I couldn't wave my hands and put my fists in my mouth to ease the pain in my gums. I couldn't smile or laugh – I couldn't do anything. I didn't even want to eat and as time went by I didn't learn to sit up or talk or walk like my little sisters had done. There was a dark shadow hanging over us all again just like in the war and nobody could see light at the end of the tunnel this time.

Of course, my mam had to get on with looking after her little family as best she could. But she was always needed outside to help on our farm and she was always sewing to make our clothes and save money. In between times she took care of me and tried to keep our house as clean as she could. She washed and brushed our stone floor while I lay on our hard couch with my grey blanket over me and I did nothing except moan.

She picked me up and I just flopped in her arms with my mouth open staring unseeingly. They had secretly begun to think that I was wrong in the head.

"She seems as daft as a brush," said Dad sadly one day as they sat for a minute by our fire having a mug of tea together. He said what nobody had dared to say out loud. I was growing up and I should have been able to do lots of things by now but I couldn't do anything.

I needed some help and Aunty Martha prayed for me "Please help her, God" – but my dad believed his saying 'God helps them that helps themselves' and he knew he had to do something.

So, he called for Doctor Moon from Ringam but the doctor just shook his big bald head, he didn't know what was wrong with me. He had never seen anything like me before. My mam and dad did not know what else to do.

Lambing time was coming up again and Dad would be sitting up all night and needed Mam to help. But Mam had to look after me and I couldn't be left. There must be something more that could be done.

Then my dad decided that there was something else he could try. He was going to get a second opinion. First, he drew what little savings he had out of his bank, then Mam wrapped me up in my grey blanket and off we went in our little car again. This time we went to Hull where there was a specialist doctor who trained down south where they had more experts than they did up north where we lived.

It was all very posh. My dad said that they walked over thick carpets in a special hospital. I was a flop of flesh all bundled up in grey. Dad wore his best funeral suit, black and rough. Mam wore her fitted navy jacket, she made it herself from an old coat carefully unpicked and turned so that it looked new. But they needn't have bothered to try and look smart because this special doctor in his soft grey suit hardly looked up at them as they walked into his room. My sad dad handed over the precious pound notes – it was so much money it would have paid for another farm hand to help with lambing.

"What do you want to know?" that posh man's voice floated softly over leather chairs Dad told me and it went over bright silk cushions and deep carpets and up to us three huddled together on a squashy sofa.

"Is she daft?" they asked him. Our brush wasn't mentioned this time.

"She is perfectly normal... mentally," he glanced up for a minute and then started to write on his notepad with his lily-white hands. He sighed a smooth sigh.

"Well, what's up with her then?" my dad burst out. His scrubbed red hands and dirt blackened nails pulled at his stiff collar.

"He means – what is wrong with her then?" corrected Mam. She was always correcting his Yorkshire way of speaking. She didn't want us kids to speak wrongly because she wanted us to do well and better ourselves. You see, because we were girls we would not have a readymade job on our farm like boys and we would have to be good at other things and get on in the world.

"It's probably a rare form of – baby poisoning," the posh private doctor said quietly but the word 'poisoning' rang out like a shot from a gun.

My mam jumped and her hold on me slackened and she nearly dropped me on the carpet. "Poisoning? What poison?"

"The poisoning was probably from teething powder – it's been withdrawn from the market now." That's all he said about my condition. Maybe the money was used up and if the doctor said more Dad thought that he would have had to pay more.

Suddenly Mam started to cry but it was not the money she was worried about.

"Will she live?" she said, her tired body crumpled now, squashing me between her bust and her knees.

"Maybe she will live, maybe she won't. In any case, there is nothing the medical profession can do now, so you must take her home."

"But how will I look after her?"

"You must do your best, it will be hard work – and," he looked at us over the top of his gold rimmed glasses, "you could pray for her of course." Then he turned away and started to look at the next person's notes.

Finally, he got up and smiled a watery smile and shook hands with them. "Good-day, good-day."

But it wasn't a good day, of course, my poor mam knew now that the powder she had rubbed on my aching gums had poisoned me. They went out of that bright room with news that was very black. We were well and truly back in the wars and there was nothing to cheer about now. The bomb that had dropped on me had left me as hollow and useless as that black bombed out tree in our paddock.

My dad walked very upright and unblinking and Mam cried gently holding me, her sick grey bundle – her baby called Victoria who was not victorious. I should not have been given that name.

Anyway, Mam and Dad took me home and carried on as they always did. But I don't think that they prayed for me like Aunty Martha did. Well I don't suppose they did because of my dad's saying about God only helping you if you helped yourself. He believed it so he just worked even harder on our farm and Mam tried even harder to look after her family and keep me alive.

Every day my mam wrapped me up in my grey blanket and, with little Gwendy following behind, she carried me outside so I could breathe some good fresh air. She carried me to our paddock to see our sheep that were lambing. But I didn't look at them. Then she took me back inside and tried to get me to eat but I didn't open my mouth.

She had fresh fish brought from Hull docks and boiled it in milk.

6

"Eat this, eat this, please eat this, oh please," she whispered. But I just lay there on our hard couch with my grey blanket over me while Mam got on with her housework.

Every day she started all over again, and wrapped me in my blanket and took me into our paddock to see our sheep. But I didn't look. She brought me back and tried to get some fish down me but I didn't open my mouth. Then she got on with her housework again with me flopping on our couch.

Then one day Mam said that when she was sweeping our stone floor, a sheep came into the house. It was a black one, our only black sheep. It must have got through a gap in the hedge and followed us all the way back to our house from our paddock.

'Ba, ba' – it burst through our door – Mam must have forgotten to shut it properly.

"Get out, get out, shoo, shoo," shouted Mam at the sheep. But the sheep would not go. It just turned tail and ran round my couch. Mam waved her brush – the one I was supposed to be as daft as.

"Go on, get out." But that sheep just turned and ran round again and my mam ran after it with her brush chasing its tail. Round and round they went, a black sheep with black currants coming out of it, followed by Mam waving her brush.

Of course, Mam was mad at the mess that the sheep was making and she ran after it faster and faster waving her brush more and prodding wildly.

"Get out, get out."

Now I suppose that must have been funny to watch because I did something I had never done before. I smiled – I actually smiled. And then I smiled again and then I laughed. I opened my mouth and forced out a funny squeaky little laugh. "Ha."

My mam stopped dead still, with her brush in the air and the sheep stopped dead still as well and they turned round and they both stared at me in amazement. Mam could not believe her ears, she told me, and she looked to see if anybody had come in and laughed that little laugh – but no, it was true, it was me and I had never laughed before.

In the end our sheep lost interest and went out the way it had come and off it ran with a 'Baa' and a few more currants dropped as it went to join its flock in our paddock. But Mam did not lose interest and she did not care about the mess now.

"Did you laugh? Did you laugh?" she shouted. "Do it again, do it again." I just stared at her not understanding. But Mam was desperate for me to laugh again. Quick as a flash she ran round and round my couch chasing a pretend sheep this time. She waved her brush (which was not so daft after all) and did some frantic pretend prods but now she was running sideways so she could watch me all the time. Round and round she went, waving and shouting and staring at me, willing me to laugh. Then I did. I laughed again.

"Ha, ha," I squeaked a bit stronger this time. Then my mam came over and laughed as well but her laugh was more like a choke and she was crying. And I laughed for the third time "Ha ha, ha," and it was like a proper laugh. Third time was lucky this time for me.

The next day our postman, called Posty, came early in the morning, as usual, on his bike from Ringam – he was the one that used to come in the war to tell us that the bombers were out. He had got a new lamp for his bike with modern batteries now and it gave a much brighter light on dark mornings.

"No better, no better," he said shaking his head at me on our couch.

"Well I think she is a bit better," said my mam, "because she laughed yesterday and that is surely a good sign and she might soon be well."

"She laughed, she laughed," shouted Mam.

But I don't think Posty was listening because as I've said, he liked bad news best. You would think that he would start to look on the bright side now the war was over and he had got a brand new bright bike lamp. But he did not. He had probably got used to bombs in the war and people were grateful for his warnings so he carried on bringing bad news out of habit. And everybody still listened eagerly.

His bad news was mostly about who was poorly, who had died and who had fallen on hard times. I bet he liked coming to our house because there had been lots of bad stuff to shout about since I was born.

"It's not a boy, not a boy!"

"She's poisoned, she's poisoned."

And today he was bringing some other bad news.

"The roads are bad, the roads are very bad," he smiled shaking his head again. "No school bus running today. It's skidded on black ice."

Well that was bad news for our Katy – she wouldn't be able to get to school on the bus and she liked school very much. In the end, Dad had to take her in our car and that made him late for rounding up his sheep. They had spent the summer eating the grass that had grown over the concrete gun stands in our Far Side field. But a few weeks ago, he had brought them into our paddock so he could keep an eye on them for the winter. If the weather was reasonable they had their lambs outside, but today the weather was too bad and Dad had to hurry. He would have to bring them all into a sheep lambing pen, which he made with bales of straw like the air raid shelter in the war, to keep the sheep safe and warm while they had their lambs.

So, when Dad got back from taking our Katy to school he rushed off to round his sheep up and put them in the lambing pen. But something was wrong and he burst into our house. My mam had just dressed me and our Gwendy was having her breakfast

"I need some help, quick!" shouted Dad. "A sheep is missing – that black one – I can't find it anywhere and it's due to lamb any time."

My mam grabbed me up in her arms then she banged on the back of our fire for Grandma to come and keep an eye on

9

our Gwendy who was still in the middle of her breakfast. Grandma's fire next door was back to back with ours and she heard Mam banging and she knew it was an emergency. She came straight away to look after Gwendy. Then Mam snatched my grey blanket and bundled me up in it. I could not be left so off I went in her arms to help Dad find our sheep. Mam never trusted anybody else to look after me, when I was little.

Dad ran across our paddock and Mam followed as best she could with me in her arms. The ground was frozen and hard.

Then all of a sudden, we saw our missing sheep with her black face stubbornly staring at that useless bombed out tree. She must have been hiding in it.

"Ci boy," shouted Dad. Mam did not even try to correct him this time even though he was not speaking properly. You see, 'ci boy' is sheep language for 'come on' and my dad was the expert in all things about farm animals. But our black sheep did not come on – she took no notice of Dad even though she would have understood very well what he was saying. They tried to shoo her and chase her towards the shelter of bales but she would not go. Then Dad got hold of her woolly back and with his strong fists pulled and pushed her towards his safe lambing pen of straw bales but she struggled free and ran back to the hollow tree.

"Shoo, shoo," shouted Mam but it made no difference the black sheep did not budge.

"You're as daft as a brush," shouted Dad at the sheep but it still made no difference. Every time he got her a little way down our paddock she broke free and struggled back to the tree. Dad grabbed her again. By now Mam was worried about me, as a cold wind had got up, so she squeezed inside the bombed-out tree with me in her arms. She got in quite easily because the bomb had forced a big wide crack all the way down to the ground.

It was dark inside but it was dry and Mam couldn't hear the wind any more. Then suddenly she heard something else.

10

'Maa, maa,' there was a little wail and Mam bent down and looked carefully amongst a pile of dry leaves and in the dim light she could just make out a little new born black lamb.

'Maa maaa,' it went again and I laughed out loud, "Haa, haaa." I was good at laughing now. But Dad wasn't laughing.

He was outside still struggling with its mother and shouting again, "You daft beggar." But she wasn't so daft – she had gone into this safe hollow tree out of the cold and biting wind to have her baby – and our bombed-out tree was not useless after all."In here!" shouted Mam at last and Dad peeped in and he couldn't believe his eyes. Then the black mother sheep pushed her head inside our little shelter to nuzzle her new born.

There was no time to lose because even though the little lamb was inside its hollow tree, it had been a long cold night and she was very weak. Quick as a flash Dad picked up the lamb and grabbing a corner of my grey blanket he rubbed it up and down with brisk sharp strokes and got the baby's blood flowing. Then dangling the lamb by her front legs, he carried her across our paddock with her back legs hanging down. Off trotted her mother without any chasing now – she just kept smelling the back legs of her little baby and anxiously followed behind Dad.

When we got to the lambing pen, at last, Dad carefully stood the lamb up and all the time its mother was fussing round and then the baby had a drink off her. So, that was a good sign that she would soon be strong and it seemed to be another good sign for me as well because from then on I started to get a bit better.

You see, after that we all went in our house to warm up and I actually drank an egg cup full of milk from some boiled fish. And soon I was eating the fish as well.

My grey blanket was thrown away because it was so old and smelly but I didn't mind one bit. I needed something brighter now I had started to come out of the wars. Mam knitted me a lovely new one, it was yellow which was better than grey because I was getting better.

It was all over, and there were no more bombs to fall and Dad and Mam sat peacefully in their chairs either side of our fire having a mug of tea. They had tried hard to help me and at last I was getting stronger.

"It's true, God helps them that helps themselves," said Dad.

"How do you know it wasn't Martha's prayers?" asked Mam – but Dad didn't answer because he wasn't there, he had gone outside to work on his farm again.

Now you know how my life began and how I was poisoned and how I started to get better because of my mam and dad's hard work and maybe Aunty Martha's prayers, not forgetting our black sheep. But there was one trouble that had not been solved. I was not a boy and never would be. I was still a girl.

That meant I had to help myself like Dad said because I believed him. I didn't mean that I thought I could help myself to actually be a boy – no – what I had to do was to try hard to be good at things and as soon as I was old enough I worked out a plan.

It was simple really. I decided to make a 'What I am good at' list. As I grew up I would collect things that I was good at for my list. So far I only had one thing to put on it – I was good at laughing – but I was sure that I would soon collect more. Then with my long list of things I could do well, I would better myself and get on in the world. My mam and dad would be proud of me even though I wasn't a boy. Victoria would be a good name for me after all. I really could be victorious.

Chapter 2

Sunnyside

It was a long time before I had something else to add to my 'What I am good at' list and I got it at Sunnyside. When Mam could spare the time, she used to take me on the bus to Sunnyside which was an old house in Ringam. It had stood forever and never changed. Mam went to see her sister, my Aunty Peggy, who lived there with The Great Aunties. Aunty Peggy and Mam always sat in the kitchen and drank tea and talked a lot about men, well really they mostly talked about one man called Henry. All I tried to do was to keep out of sight of The Great Aunties – Dolly and Dilly – because I was a bit scared of them. I was scared of Great Aunty Dolly because she was strict and I was scared of Great Aunty Dilly because she was deaf and dumb.

I wasn't scared of my Aunty Peggy because I thought that she was a very interesting person. For a start, she had worked on a teleprinter in the war and secretly got messages in code from the enemy and passed them on to somebody who could crack codes and find out what the enemy was saying. I thought that it would be a wonderful thing to be good at cracking codes.

As you know I had decided to be good at quite a lot of things but I only had one thing on my list so far. I needed a lot more things so I could better myself and get on in the world and make Mam and Dad proud of me even though I wasn't the boy they wanted.

I sat thinking about being good at things and watched as Aunty Peggy blew smoke into the air. I didn't know any other lady who smoked – I told you she was interesting. My dad smoked a pipe but that was different, most men smoked pipes, ladies didn't smoke – except my Aunty Peggy. I used to watch in amazement as she casually puffed on her cigarette and if she was in their front room she pressed her stub on the ivy leaf ashtray that was on the mantelpiece. There was a little brass wren that sat on a stalk of the ivy leaf and it seemed to lift its eyebrows in disapproval, when Aunty Peggy smoked, and so did Great Aunty Dolly.

I was scared of Great Aunty Dolly, as I have said, because she was strict but Aunty Peggy didn't seem so worried about her strictness. Mind you Mam told me that once a long time ago Aunty Peggy *had* been scared of her Aunty Dolly just like I was now. This is what Mam told me and I think that it is a very sad story.

When Aunty Peggy was born, her home was crowded with her young brothers and sisters but her Aunty Dolly and Aunty Dilly had no children and they had plenty of room at Sunnyside. So, it was decided that Peggy should go and live with them and they would bring her up as their daughter and be her mother. I suppose it was nice for them because they hadn't got married and they would be lonely without any children of their own. It would be nice for little Peggy as well because she would be like an only child. And that is how it was, just the three of them at Sunnyside. But then the war broke out and Peggy was a young woman by then and she left and went to do war work in an office. She walked through the gate at Sunnyside with her little brown suitcase tightly buckled, and went down Green Lane to a secret place down south. Young Peggy loved her interesting work and passed secret messages, from the enemy, on to a clever man called Henry who was very good at cracking codes and finding out what the enemy was saying. Of course, Henry was handsome and looked dashing in his uniform and the young Peggy fell madly in love with him and he fell in love with her. When the war was won, they would surely marry and be together for ever and ever.

And so naturally one day Peggy brought Henry to Ringam. They walked, arm in arm and in love, down Green Lane and through the gate to Sunnyside. Then Henry went down on one

14

knee in the garden where the big poppies brushed their bright floppy petals all over his trousers. He was proposing to Aunty Peggy. Of course, she said "Yes," straight away because she loved him dearly. He was quite a bit older than she was but that wasn't a problem. My mam said that he was probably a bit of a father figure what with her being brought up in a house with just women and it would add to the attraction.

When Henry had got his answer from young Peggy he went straight to Aunty Dolly who was sitting bolt upright in her chair and he told her that he loved Peggy and they wanted to be together always. They never wanted to be parted and so he asked for her hand in marriage.

"No," shouted Great Aunty Dolly. "No, no, that would never do."

How could she? What was wrong with him? Marrying a man so much older than you was a bit unusual for a woman but it wasn't a real problem to either of them. Well no, it wasn't but there was another great problem and it was that Henry had been married before and was now divorced. Aunty Dolly would not allow him another wedding and as I have told you she was very strict and her word was 'Law' at Sunnyside. To be divorced was a disgrace and against all Dolly's strong Methodist Chapel principles. Peggy could not marry a divorced man and that was the end of that.

When young Peggy heard the news, she ran out into the garden crying and Henry ran after her trying to put his arms round her. But it was no good and she shook him off. Peggy was scared of her Aunty Dolly in those days and felt that she should do as she was told. So finally, after a lot of crying and sitting in the garden with the poppy petals falling on her shoes she said her 'Goodbye' to her beloved Henry and with her eyes full of tears she waved him off down Green Lane.

That was the end of Mam's story to me and I thought that it was even sadder because Aunty Peggy never married anybody else. Henry was her one true love. She was often sad and didn't laugh much and she got a bit hardened after all she went through in the war and she started to stand up to Aunty Dolly.

When the war was finally over Peggy dutifully came back to live at Sunnyside, then went to work in Hull. I found that very interesting because I only went to Hull when I had to go for a hospital check. My mam and me went every month to see how my poisoning was getting on. It was getting along quite well though I was still small for my age and I was 'susceptible to illness,' said Mam. I didn't like going to Hull at all. It was all bombed out and we had to pick our way through the rubble of bricks and mortar, but that was where Aunty Peggy went every day leaving her aunties at Sunnyside and they passed the day gardening, if it was fine weather.

The Great Aunties wore wide rimmed, bright coloured sun hats so that they looked just like their big nodding poppies. Great Aunty Dolly would dig a hole for a plant and firm it in on one side of their path and then Great Aunty Dilly would come along and dig it up and put it on other side. For some reason, Dilly was not scared of Dolly and Dolly did not say 'No, no that would never do,' to Dilly. My dad said that they were like two sides of the same coin. Anyway, their plants always grew and grew and then flowered and flowered and their fruit and vegetables dripped over and fell into your hand as you went past. Even their little bantam hens at the bottom of the garden laid hundreds of eggs for The Great Aunties' breakfasts – cooked sunny side down for Dolly and sunny side up for Dilly. And every day Dolly fed the hens with corn and Dilly gave them water. So, their garden was always full to bursting with things to look at and things to eat.

Sometimes The Great Aunties would be in their kitchen cooking things they had grown. Great Aunty Dilly turned their cooker up to hot and then Great Aunty Dolly sighed and heaved herself out of her chair and turned the cooker down to cool. And so it went on until dinner was cooked to delicious perfection.

Mostly though, The Great Aunties were together in their front room having cups of tea while the little brass wren watched from its ivy perch on the mantelpiece. They sat on opposite sides of the fire just as they always had and always would.

As I have said, I was scared of Great Aunty Dilly as well, not because she was strict, but because Dad said she was deaf and dumb. She was very thin – well, to tell the truth she was skinny and she was so skinny that I couldn't see how all her innards fitted into her. Come to think of it she was even skinner than me, which is saying something. Her head was big for her little body and her face looked funny with her smooth cheeks caved in because she hardly had any teeth. But the worst thing of all for me was that because she could not say proper words, I couldn't tell what she was saying.

You see, even though Dad said that she was dumb, it was not true that she couldn't talk. What he meant was that she could not talk how we all talked. But she used to talk in her own way all the time. When she said something to me it just sounded like 'goo gaa gii' and I couldn't crack the code to find out what she was saying. Words came out through her nose and got mixed up with air going in. Aunty Peggy understood her of course – I expect Henry had taught her a bit about cracking codes in the war – but I just could not understand and that made her scary for me.

When Great Aunty Dilly said something to me I didn't know what to do. Sometimes I used to smile and nod pretending I understood what she said. But she knew I didn't understand because she was very clever. Even though she was deaf and 'dumb' and hadn't been to school, Mam said that she was self-taught and knew what was what. And it was true because she would look at me with her big brown eyes and there would be no escape – she knew the truth. I could of course pretend I hadn't heard her – but I'd tried that once and that didn't work either because she kept saying it again and again.

'Goo, gaa, gii' – louder and louder she shouted so I must hear her. How scary she was – I just had to make sure she never got a chance to talk to me. I had to keep out of her way. So, there we were, I had to keep away from both my great aunties

17

because Dilly was deaf and 'dumb' and Dolly was too strict. And it was strange because even though they were always together, you probably know by now that they were exact opposites even in their looks.

Dolly looked very different from thin Great Aunty Dilly. When Dolly walked, she was slow and deliberate and when she sat down she filled her chair with her big body. Her round hairy cheeks bulged out and her sausage fingers were sparkling with jewelled rings. She wasn't deaf like Aunty Dilly either. Her hearing was so good she heard everything and saw everything. Well, that is not quite true because she didn't hear or see me sneak upstairs, which I often did at Sunnyside. I dashed past the front room door and tiptoed up the wooden stairs because if she had seen me she would have shouted 'No, no,' so I just had to sneak about very carefully indeed.

One day when I sneaked upstairs at Sunnyside, Mam and Aunty Peggy were talking about men again in the kitchen and Great Aunty Dolly and Great Aunty Dilly were sitting in their chairs in the front room. I had to be very careful and not make a sound as I crept up the stairs unnoticed. Up and up I went into a dark corridor that seemed to go on forever all along the back of their house and at the end was the little brown suitcase. I had seen it before but this time I wanted to look inside. I undid the buckles and lifted the lid carefully. Out came a waft of secret hidden mysteries of long ago. I put my hands in and felt around and my fingers curled round something soft. I carefully lifted it out to look at it as best I could in the dim light. It was a little black velvet purse embroidered with bight poppies. I held it to my face and felt its powder puff softness. I ran my fingers along the shiny petals and it was then that I felt something hard inside.

I knew that opening somebody's purse was a dreadful thing but I just could not resist. I lifted the flap and then turned round guiltily because what I was doing was unforgivable but nobody was there to see. I tipped the purse and out rolled a farthing with a little brown wren on one side. At the top, there was a little ring fastened to it so it could go on a chain if you had one.

'Creak'. What was that? I was sure I heard a noise and I peered into the gloomy passage. But I couldn't see anything. So I felt again in the purse and pulled out an old photo of a handsome man in uniform.

'Creak'. There it was again. This time I was sure I saw a little shadow like a bird fluttering but after that everything was quiet and still again. I was getting a bit nervous now so hastily I shoved everything back and crept quietly downstairs.

My mam was still with Aunty Peggy in their kitchen and they were whispering.

"What did I miss?" asked Aunty Peggy. "I should have married him."

"But you couldn't – Aunty Dolly said 'No, no'," answered Mam leaning forward and holding Aunty Peggy's hand.

"I should have stood up to her – I would now."

I didn't hear Mam's answer because I skipped off down the garden path on my own.

But I wasn't alone, disaster had struck, because Great Aunty Dilly had come out into the garden as well. I could see her bobbing along and I could hear her nasal call. She was following me. I ran along the path where wet poppy petals flopped onto my socks, as I brushed past. I ran to the bottom of the garden where little bantam hens laid their eggs. I ran on past the vegetables and on faster and faster but whenever I turned round she was still in hot pursuit and gaining on me. I ran on again – my plan was to escape on to Green Lane. Out of breath, I stopped at the gate, which led to freedom, and turned to look at her. She was half hidden by the pear tree but I could see her face and she was smiling a wide gappy smile.

"Boo," she said gently and laughed, peeping out from the tree trunk. I knew how to answer her now, no need to pretend. I needn't have run away.

"Boo," I answered and I laughed relieved – this was easy. But I hadn't got away so lightly because she spoke again.

"Goo gaa gii," she said holding her hand out towards me. Desperately I pretended I understood and nodded my head but her brown eyes stared deep into mine and even when I looked down I just knew she was still staring at me.

"Yoo, gaa, gii," she insisted, so this time I looked straight at her and pretended I hadn't heard. But I knew it wouldn't work it never did because she was too clever to fall for that one.

"Yoo, haa, gii," she said again even louder. Then it struck me. That shadow I saw when I was poking around in that suitcase must have been Aunty Dilly, that creak must have been her little brown shoes on a floorboard. She had seen everything. Mam always said that if you were deaf then your sight gets better to compensate. And it must have been true because even though Great Aunty Dolly hadn't seen me go upstairs Great Aunty Dilly had – and she had followed me. She must have seen me open that purse and now she must be telling me off.

I licked my dry mouth.

"I'm sorry I shouldn't have been looking in that suitcase and especially not in that purse. I'm really sorry, I won't do it again." I did actions hanging my head and looking very sorry. But she didn't move and just stayed there holding her hand out. And come to think of it she didn't look cross. In fact, she was still smiling her big gappy smile. And why was she holding her hand out? I looked more carefully and there on her tiny palm was that farthing, that brown wren coin snuggling against her warm wrinkled skin. I watched her face and she was smiling even more and pushing her flat palm towards me.

"Yoo ha itt," she sent her words at me with great effort her head bowing with every sound that came out of her nose. She kept smiling and holding that precious coin out to me.

"For me?" I mouthed wide-eyed pointing to myself. She nodded and I went towards her and carefully picked the farthing up between my finger and thumb. Oh, I would always treasure this. I turned it over in my hand to look at the little brown wren and then the strict King – like Dilly and Dolly – two sides of the same coin. I held it tight in my hand and smiled.

But Great Aunty Dilly wanted me to look at something else. In her other hand, she held that little black velvet purse covered in poppies – she brushed it gently on her hollow cheek. Then she pretended to hold a needle in her hand and pretended to thread it and did some pretend embroidery.

"You did that?" I mouthed again pointing to her and then to the embroidery and she nodded and nodded and smiled and smiled. Then she nodded and nodded again.

It was then that she stopped smiling and held out the old photograph – it was of the handsome man in uniform.

"Is that Henry?" I shouted and she looked at me sadly and I knew that it was. Then she put it back in her purse and off she flew down the path towards the house in her little brown shoes.

I followed her and grinned because I was pleased with myself, even though I was a bit sad about handsome Henry it was all a very long time ago. You see, I had been able to tell what Great Aunty Dilly was saying and I could add that to my 'What I am good at' list. I had cracked the secret code somehow. I was thrilled and of course I had my little farthing coin to treasure forever. I burst into the house.

"Look what Aunty Dilly gave me," I showed my coin excitedly to Mam.

"You can't take that, you know you must never take money from anybody, give it back!" She took my precious coin from my hand.

"Gii gaa gi goo ge," said Great Aunty Dilly bobbing about in agitation, I could tell that she meant 'I gave it to her' I could tell what she was saying now and I was surprised that I ever found it difficult. But Mam couldn't tell what she was saying and she pushed my coin back into Great Aunty Dilly's hand.

"She has given it to her, she wants her to have it," said Aunty Peggy and Great Aunty Dilly nodded and nodded so much that I thought her big head would come off her thin little neck. Then she gave me the farthing back and I put it in my pocket where it was safe and everything was all right again.

But one day when we went to Sunnyside things weren't all right. My Great Aunty Dilly was not there – she wasn't in the garden digging up plants, she wasn't in the kitchen turning the oven up, she wasn't in the front room sitting by the fire in her little chair. My mam said that she had crossed over and that meant that she would not be coming back. Sunnyside had changed forever and even Great Aunty Dolly could not make it stay the same by saying,

'No, no, that would never do.'

Her beloved sister was buried in the Methodist graveyard wearing her little brown leather shoes.

Aunty Dilly had gone but Aunty Dolly hadn't – well they were opposites after all. And now Great Aunty Dolly just slumped near the fire in her chair which suddenly seemed too big for her. Even her rings lost their sparkle as she stared at the little empty chair opposite and sometimes when she thought no one was looking (but I was and so was the little wren on the mantelpiece) she got that little black poppy purse out of her handbag and looked at it and gently brushed it against her hairy cheek. I sometimes wondered if Great Aunty Dolly ever thought about Henry and Peggy. And I wondered if she was sorry she had parted them, now that she knew what it was like to lose the one you love.

Now when we went to Sunnyside, Mam still talked a bit to Aunty Peggy and sometimes I ran aimlessly round the garden. But mostly we just sat in their front room with Great Aunty Dolly and that little empty chair. We did nothing and said nothing while Dolly shrivelled before our eyes and her spare skin dropped in folds round her ankles.

Then one day while I was running aimlessly in their garden again with nothing to do – an old man with grey hair came down Green Lane – he opened the gate and went up the path to the door. He knocked gently. I watched what happened next from behind the pear tree. And what happened was that Aunty Peggy came to the door and stood there in silence. Then she shrieked and threw her arms round the man and laughed and laughed a great wide open mouthed laugh.

"Henry," she shouted. "Oh Henry."

I must say I was a bit disappointed with this Henry – he was not one bit good looking like in that photo now that he was even older and not in uniform. But Aunty Peggy didn't seem to notice and Henry came to stay in Ringam and went every day to Sunnyside to dig the garden and feed the hens and help look after Great Aunty Dolly.

My mam and Aunty Peggy talked and talked in the kitchen again like they used to.

"What did I miss? Tell me it all…"

"I can't I'm too embarrassed you'll have to find out for yourself."

"I will soon," laughed Aunty Peggy with her new wide mouthed laugh.

They got married at Ringam Methodist Chapel – the new young vicar didn't mind too much that Uncle Henry was divorced and in any case, said Mam, times had changed. Aunty Dolly didn't go to the wedding of course; she stayed at Sunnyside staring at the empty little chair. But at least she didn't say 'No, no' this time, maybe she knew better now.

I went to the wedding and I must say that I was very sorry to see that Aunty Peggy didn't wear a big white dress – she wore a simple brown suit – which Mam said was more appropriate all things considered. Even so I thought that Aunty Peggy looked very dull but Uncle Henry didn't seem to be worried and just stared happily into his bride's eyes.

After the wedding, they hurried back to Sunnyside. When I went to see them they were both looking after Aunty Dolly as best they could and put thicker shawls round her shoulders and fluffier slippers on her feet. But Dolly just got colder and colder. I watched them make her lovely tempting meals from the garden fruit and vegetables and served her fresh eggs sunny side down but she just got thinner and thinner. I saw her rings fall off her skinny fingers and Uncle Henry put them on the ivy leaf for the little wren to look after. Aunty Peggy had stopped smoking now but Dolly didn't even notice. In fact, she stopped noticing everything until one day my mam told me that Great Aunty Dolly had 'crossed over' and she was with Dilly again at last. They buried her in her fluffy slippers next to her sister. And it says on their grave stone:

'Dolly and Dilly.

Together again.

Never more to be parted.'

Aunty Peggy thought of that saying and I thought that it was good because that meant Peggy and Henry as well.

There were a lot more changes at Sunnyside after all that and there was nobody to say 'No, no, that would never do.'

But some things stayed the same because the big bright poppies seeded everywhere and they grew again and again. And there were hundreds of them flowering and flowering on both sides of the path.

Chapter 3

Our Farm

Sunnyside had to change to keep up with the times and so did our farm. While I was trying to get another thing on my 'What I am good at' list, my dad and his brother Uncle Sid, who lived next door with his family and Grandma, were working harder and harder to change things for the better. Sometimes though, when things changed there were problems that had to be sorted.

One problem happened before I was born and my dad told me the story as I went with him to collect our cows from Bottom Field so that they could be milked. One day Dad bought a cart horse from a dealer in Ringam. She was a lovely red-brown coloured horse and she looked fine and well, with shiny mane and strong muscles, but when Dad coupled her to a cart they found out that she wasn't all she seemed, in fact she was no use at all.

"She's going backwards!" shouted Uncle Sid, giving their new horse a smack on her backside with his strong hand.

"Walk on!" shouted my dad getting worried.

But the horse kept on taking its slow heavy steps in the wrong direction, she kept on walking backwards. Dad had bought this horse to bring the hay in and she was turning out to be a problem. She was fine when she wasn't coupled up to the cart but as soon as she was in the shafts she went backwards.

"Whoa!" Dad shouted. "Walk on, not back." And he pulled on her reins but the whites of her eyes showed and she would not walk on.

The sun shone from a blue sky but our barometer was pointing to 'Change' and that meant more problems because you could already see a storm getting up over the Humber. Big black clouds were boiling up. The hay would be spoilt if it rained and they were relying on that new horse but still it walked backwards.

My dad had given a big cheque to the dealer for that horse and now she would not walk forwards with the cart. They tried everything – putting oats in front of her, smacking her on the backside, shouting and calling but nothing worked. That horse would not pull a cart and that was the end of that.

I bet Dad's face was as black as the thunder clouds over the Humber as he sweated over that horse.

"Walk on, you daft beggar," he shouted but he wasn't getting anywhere.

Then Uncle Sid suddenly saw that they were going about things the wrong way altogether and he shouted, "We've got to stop the cheque. Quick." My dad did not know about things like that but Uncle Sid did, because he read the newspapers and he knew what to do.

There was no time to lose. They rushed off to their bank in Ringam. And they were only just in time to stop the cheque. At the end of that day the money would have been in the hands of the horse dealer – he would have cashed it and that would have been difficult.

You see, when they took the horse back to the horse dealer he said that he had never had any trouble with her before and that she was a perfectly good horse. But she was no good to us. Anyway, Dad and Uncle Sid had their money back and the horse dealer had his horse back and there was nothing more to be said. They hurried home to the hay that was still in the field. They had to get that hay in somehow and so they had to go back to Dobbin.

Dobbin was our old horse and he was in retirement – he had got too weak to do his job and he had been put out to grass. He lived in his field called Hoss Paster (Mam said we should say 'Horse Pasture' but we never did) and my dad put reins on Dobbin and fastened him into his cart shafts and shouted "Walk on" and then the horse's massive bulk slowly plodded down our lane. He knew what to do but he couldn't hurry he had to take his time, stopping off for a rest and bit of grass to chew at the side of the road. That was no good at all. And of course, the storm came and they didn't get all the hay in. This made Dad think, because he was trying to change our farm for the better and then found the horse that walked backwards was a red herring. My dad said that a red herring is something that is no use even though you might think at first that it is. So, that was the end of Dad's story about the horse that walked backwards.

Uncle Sid knew how to take our farm forwards. He knew how to change things for the better. He bought our first tractor and it was bright red, even brighter than the horse that went backwards. He called it Red Herring for a bit of a joke because that horse was a joke and in fact all horses on farms were red herrings now that we had changed to tractors. Soon they heard that the Ringam horse dealer had gone out of business because nobody wanted working horses on farms now. Everything was going forwards and changing for the better.

It was the same in our milking shed; everything was being updated. Dad had built up a big herd and it would take far too long to milk by hand so we had our old cowshed modernised and the latest milking machines fitted.

Every day Dad went down to Bottom Field to fetch our cows where they had been eating grass all day. They were waiting at the gate and when he opened it they rushed up our lane making a black mist of dust and flies, just like that thunder cloud moving steadily nearer. And then you could hear them mooing and gathering speed till they were in our yard waiting to be milked.

Our cowshed had been scrubbed clean to get rid of all germs and was ready and waiting. My dad was always worried about germs getting into the herd or the milk. We relied on the milk cheque from the Dairy and the herd had to be clear of illness, and the milk had to be pure.

"Come on you daft beggars," shouted Dad and he slapped the cows' backsides and they rushed into their stalls. He often called his animals 'daft beggars' but he didn't mean it – except with that backwards walking horse of course.

My favourite cow was one called Daisy – they all had to have names nowadays. The black and white pattern of every cow had to be drawn on a post card and sent to the people in charge down south and they registered it for our pedigree herd. They even told us what letter the name had to begin with. Daisy's year was D of course and there was Doris and Dolores as well. Every year it was the next letter of the alphabet. I liked Daisy because she was easy to spot with her pattern a bit like a daisy on her forehead. I watched while the cows were tied up with a chain round their necks ready for milking. I could already hear the panting and pulsing of the milking machine impatient to get on with its job. But first our cows had to be sprayed.

My dad sprayed at their tails to get rid of flies. Blue bottles and all sorts of insects sat on muck full of germs then came crashing into our milking shed buzzing and banging into windows and then landing on our cows and in our milk if we were not careful.

But we were careful, every place where germs could be was scrubbed and every fly that we could see was sprayed. After milking, all the frothy milk was heaved off in shiny buckets and then poured through a thick filter and then into sterilized milk cans. On went the lid and these cans were lifted outside onto our milk stand to wait for a lorry to take them to the Dairy. Then we would get a regular cheque in the post brought by Posty, our postman. So long as we kept on getting plenty of milk from the cows we got a milk cheque. The more milk we had the bigger the cheque. And to get more milk we had to have a bull.

In a deep dark corner of our fold yard there was a pen that was more like a cage with bars. Not a pen like Dad built out of straw bales for our sheep when they were lambing. Oh, no, this one had much stronger walls and they were about ten bricks deep, and one wall was made of iron bars so thick that I couldn't get my fingers round them. The iron door was kept tight shut by about ten massive bolts. And inside this deep dark cage Big Billy bull lived. He snorted and blew smoke and went cross-eyed with anger and bellowed like thunder at being caged up. My dad looked after Billy and went in the cage to clean him out and keep him free from germs – I didn't know how he dared to go in with our dangerous Big Billy but he did. We all kept away when Dad was in there just in case Billy got angry and then got Dad.

Sometimes, at weekends, my sister Gwendy and me used to play with Terry and Stewy who were my cousins from next door. Their dad was Uncle Sid and their mam was Aunty Vera and they lived with Grandma. When nobody was looking, us kids used to go and see Big Billy. We used to tease him and sometimes Terry threw a bit of a brick or a bit of a log into his pen. We loved Terry doing this – he was always so daring and did what we were too frightened to do. But Billy didn't like it at all and he got mad and we stared open-mouthed as he scraped the concrete floor with his foot and went cross-eyed and blew smoke out of his nostrils. We loved to hear his powerful bellow like thunder, while we were safe on the other side of the bars. Big Billy was the most powerful animal we had – he was even more powerful than Dobbin was when he was young. But we didn't want Big Billy for his power, we didn't want him to pull carts or anything – no, his power was not important and it was no use anyway because he couldn't do anything because he was always caged up.

He couldn't do anything till Dad gave him a cow. I watched Daisy go in with Big Billy and there was hardly enough room for two of them in his pen and so they squashed up together. I could see the whites showing in Daisy's eyes. Then very quickly Big Billy did the only thing he could do. He got on Daisy's back and Dad said that he did 'the business'. Then Daisy was let out with a clanging and crashing of ten bolts. Then it was Doris' turn and then Dolores and so on. There was always plenty of business for Big Billy to do.

After that Daisy and the rest were 'in calf' and after a bit of time I saw Daisy have her baby in our fold yard. She was mooing all night and when I stood on our bedroom windowsill and looked out I could see two white feet sticking out of her backside while her body heaved. Then at last a sloppy calf dropped out of her and Daisy licked it clean. They looked lovely together.

But then her calf was taken away from her.

'Mam, maamm,' shouted Daisy's calf from her black wooden pen in our calf shed.

'Mo, moo,' shouted Daisy with the whites of her eyes showing but nobody took any notice.

You see, after Daisy had her calf she would make more milk and as you know, the more milk we sold the bigger our milk cheque would be. So Daisy's calf was not allowed any of his mother's milk – not even her very first milk. This was special milk and it was full of natural medicine for Daisy's little calf which it did not get. But we couldn't sell this first milk because it was yellow and lumpy – and it must not go in our pure white smooth milk, so us kids ate it. Mam made a lumpy pie for us and it was quite good to eat. It would have been good for our calves and protected them from diseases but they didn't need it because we could give them medicines nowadays if they got sick. I sometimes thought that the medicines could be like my teething powder and could poison them. But I needn't have worried because our calves were well and grew stronger and stronger on their powdered milk mixed with water.

But even though our calves were strong I was sure that they missed their mams. Daisy's calf just stood there on his long spindly legs in his dark wooden pen shouting 'Maaa' most of the day. I was sorry for him and often went to see him and I held his bucket while he drank his watery milk. He licked my hand with his big pink tongue and I rubbed the rough shiny hair on his black and white head. Then suddenly one day Daisy's calf was taken to Hull market and was sold because he was a boy. On our farm, we liked our baby calves to be girls (with human babies it was the other way round). We would have been able to keep Daisy's calf if it had been a girl because when it grew up she could have joined our milking herd. But he was not a girl and we did not want another bull – Big Billy could easily cope with all the business. Boy calves had to be sold and my dad said that they sometimes went abroad to be eaten. I thought that Daisy would miss her little calf even more now but Dad said that she had probably forgotten about it.

"Out of sight out of mind," he said. And he said it again the next day when Dobbin went away.

A big lorry drew up in our yard and we had to go down our lane to fetch Dobbin. I loved going for Dobbin, his cart was in Hoss Paster with him, and Dad got a halter and reins on him and backed him into the shafts. Dobbin looked at us with his big brown eyes and chewed a bit of grass. Then Dad and me sat with our legs dangling over the front of the cart and Dad sat holding the reins. I wished I could hold his reins but I was not strong enough. Dobbin was not very strong either, not because he had been poisoned like me, but because he was very old. He had to stop for a rest a few times. He thought he had all the time in the world but he hadn't. Our farm was changing fast.

"Walk on," Dad shouted and Dobbin slowly walked on and up our lane into our yard.

"Whoa," Dad shouted and Dobbin stood still. Then something awful happened. Dad uncoupled the cart and led Dobbin up a ramp into the lorry that had just come. I saw Dobbin turn to look at us before the doors were slammed shut. The whites of his eyes were showing in terror, he didn't know where he was going. The lorry rumbled off and Dobbin was on the way to his death at the knacker's yard. I watched sadly as the lorry chugged further up our lane then at the same time I saw another new tractor hurtling down, splattering the knacker's yard lorry with mud. Uncle Sid was driving and Terry was sitting near him on the mudguard waving and laughing as they bounced along at top speed.

Our second tractor was blue and Uncle Sid called it Blue Bottle for another joke because of all the flies that we sprayed so they couldn't spread germs. Now we had two tractors, Red Herring and Blue Bottle and they raced about all day long on our land pulling all our new implements on our fields. They went very fast so that we would get more and more crops, quicker and quicker. Dobbin's old cart with shafts was chopped up for firewood, we wouldn't need that any more now we had changed to tractors.

Big Billy was getting ready for a change as well because Dad decided to put him in a show. First, Dad put a ring in his nose – I don't know how he did it but he did, while Billy bellowed like thunder. Then he washed Big Billy down to make his black and white marks clear and clean, like a map of a new land on his back. Big Billy was not pleased with all this and kept on bellowing and snorting smoke out his nostrils. But my dad wasn't frightened and just said, "Come on, you daft beggar." Then he took Billy off to his first Agricultural Show and when he came home Billy went back in his cage and snorted smoke and bellowed again but with pride this time. You see, he got second prize and had a silver rosette to prove it. Well, after that he went to heaps of shows and won heaps of rosettes. One day he would get first prize and win a gold rosette we just knew he would. My dad got a big picture frame and put all his rosettes behind glass and hung it in our cowshed just to remind our cows how lucky they were. But then we started to get some more problems that had to be solved and they were even harder to put right than the horse that walked backwards.

One problem was that my dad lost our milk cheque – Posty had delivered it as usual and Dad had picked it up to take to the bank in Ringam. But first he had to finish milking and then he cleaned the cowshed out. Then he jumped in our car ready to go to Ringam and felt in his pocket but the cheque was not there. He searched everywhere but he couldn't find it. I looked for it as well, maybe I wasn't very strong but I was sure I could find that cheque. If only I could find it, I could put – finding cheques – on my 'What I am good at' list. Oh, I longed to find that cheque. Then I could solve Dad's problem and he would be very pleased with me even though I wasn't a boy. It would also mean that I would have three things that I was good at. I went and looked in the empty envelope, I looked at the path from our house to the cowshed and I looked in the cowshed. I couldn't find it but it never went out of my mind – so out of sight out of mind was not true for our milk cheque.

The next problem was that Big Billy got sick even though as you know we washed and cleaned everywhere and sprayed for flies every day – we did our very best to keep the germs away. But Big Billy somehow did get germs. Our vet came from Ringam and left some medicine for Dad to give to Big Billy. But Billy wouldn't take it.

"Come on, you daft beggar," shouted Dad and he rolled up his sleeves and forced the medicine down sick Billy's throat with his bare hands. Then we just had to wait and see. It was hard to wait on our modern farm with our tractors rushing up and down and milking machines panting and pulsing twice a day. And Dad and Uncle Sid hadn't a minute to spare. Big Billy being sick was a big problem – we needed to put more cows in his cage to get more calves and get more milk and more milk cheques. And oh, I tried to stop thinking about the milk and that lost cheque but I couldn't and there was worse to come.

Big Billy dropped down dead and the modern medicines were not as good as I thought. Posty heard the news of course – he always heard bad news and I bet he went all round Gum shouting, "Bull's dead – Big Billy's dead!"

I went to look through the bars of Dead Billy's cage and he was all bloated with his legs sticking out filling his cage with stinking flesh. Then flies got in and they danced about in a dirty black cloud all over Dead Billy. The vet warned us to keep away and get him buried as soon as we could. Billy's disease could be passed on to us or other animals on our farm if we didn't hurry up. Daisy and Doris and Dolores could die and all the little claves in the black calf shed could die. Then all would be lost and all the hard work would be ruined and our farm would not be able to change for the better any more. We might even have to change back to milking by hand with just a little herd. And we might have to sell our tractors now Billy could not do his business. I couldn't help thinking that the lost milk cheque could be our last.

It's not a boy!

Our Gwendy and me stood on our bedroom windowsill and stared out of the window while Dead Billy's body was taken on a trailer pulled by our new blue tractor. Billy's funeral procession went down our lane to Hoss Paster, our Bobby ('Call him the policeman,' said Mam but we didn't) who was from Ringam went in front to make sure Billy was buried properly and then there was our vet and Uncle Sid and Dad — it was very serious. Terry followed on behind, his head was bowed and his cap was in his hand. Then he looked up and saw us at our window and he grinned and waved with his cap but I couldn't wave. I could hardly take my eyes off Dead Billy's bloated body as it rolled slowly from side to side on our cart under a cover of sacking. I could just see his dead nose sticking out with his big ring hanging there useless, no more shows for him and no gold rosette for first prize — ever. He was buried six feet under in Hoss Paster with the ghost of Dobbin for company and Blue Bottle revved backwards and forwards over his grave to squash it down and make sure those germs didn't get out — if they weren't out already. Dead Billy's rosettes behind the glass began to curl and fall in a pile at the bottom of the frame.

But there was even worse to come; there was another problem because I heard Mam and Dad talking one night when they thought I was in bed. I was listening at the bottom of our stairs. I heard that my dad had his hand down Billy's throat when he was giving that medicine and he had a cut on his arm and germs could have got in and Blue Bottle going backwards and forwards was too late to help my dad. Doctor Moon from Ringam just shook his big bald head and said Dad had to wait and watch that scratch. If it swelled Dad could die like Billy and he would be all stiff and bloated. I crept to bed in misery. What if my poor dad did die? Would it be out of sight out of mind then like Dobbin and our calves sold at Hull market to go abroad? And how could we look after our cow herd without Dad? Even when I grew up I wouldn't be as big and strong as a man because I wasn't a boy and we just could not manage. Our lives depended on what happened to that scratch.

I can tell you I secretly watched that scratch on my dad's arm every waking minute every day as he worked on our farm with his shirtsleeves rolled up. But my dad wasn't frightened he just got on with his work like he always did as if his scratch was no problem.

And it was no problem in the end because none of our other animals got sick, and my dad did not die and soon everything started changing for the better again.

We got stronger fly sprays for our cowshed and Dad scrubbed Dead Billy's cage out time and time again with all the latest and better disinfectants. And my dad said that there were some even better medicines out now for his animals if they got sick.

Then a cheque came from our insurance company for Dead Billy. And then we got an even bigger and better bull and he had a very fancy pedigree name. I didn't suppose they were at 'W' yet down south but we secretly called our new bull William because Billy was short for William and our Wonderful William was not short of anything. He was a real champion and Dad said that we'd better clear out that old frame for some bigger and better rosettes. William would get first prize for sure and it would be a gold rosette. All our problems were sorted – except one. What had happened to that milk cheque? That was one thing that still had not gone out of my mind. I wished again and again that I could find it and put it on my 'What I am good at' list.

Then ages after on a warm spring day when the barometer was pointing to 'Fair', I went into our cowshed to clear out the old rosettes like Dad said. They were covered in dead flies now – the flies had crept in there behind the glass to hide from the even stronger killer spray and then they couldn't find their way out and died anyway. I stood looking at the mess and then suddenly I saw it. A little corner of white paper with writing on was sticking out from behind the frame. And when I lifted the frame, the paper corner grew into a longer piece of paper and it fluttered to the ground – it was the lost milk cheque. I put – finding cheques – on my 'What I am good at' list straight away and I ran to my dad and pushed the cheque in his hand. He looked at it and smiled but he didn't seem as pleased as I thought he would be. I couldn't understand it because, after all, I had sorted our last problem.

"Oh," he said casually, "I remember now – that's where I put it, behind the frame for safe keeping, when I was cleaning out cowshed." But you see, it had not been a problem after all because Dad told me that Uncle Sid had phoned the Dairy as soon as the cheque was lost and they had cancelled the old cheque and then sent us a new one. So there had been no last problem to sort.

"You haven't been looking for it, have you? You daft beggar," Dad said smiling at me. "It's just a red herring now." Then he tore the old cheque up and threw the pieces into the air. And a warm gust got up and blew the bits of paper into a white cloud and it danced a happy little dance down our lane to Hoss Paster and then on to Bottom Field where our cows were waiting at the gate to come up for milking again.

Chapter 4

Helen in Pink

Our tractors had brought change to our farm and soon something happened to me that changed my life for ever. I had to go to school. My long days at home with my mam and dad on our farm had ended. My mam said that I would learn to be good at things and I thought that would help me get on in the world and better myself. Maybe I could get some more things on my 'What I am good at' list and that was very important to me as you know.

My mam must have thought school was very important as well because she made me a new dress. First, she went to a remnant shop in Ripsea and bought some material – this was leftover scraps that nobody else wanted. But Mam was so good at sewing that in the end she changed a remnant into a dress for me. She chose brown and that was nice because it reminded me of my Great Aunty Dilly who always wore brown like the little wren on the farthing she gave me. (I tried not to think of Aunty Peggy's disappointing wedding suit which was also brown.) Mam rattled on her sewing machine all that night. I could hear it as I fell asleep, rattle, rattle went her machine at first then it took off and 'rrrrrrrr' it went at top speed. And in the morning, there was my dress to try on.

If you looked carefully you could see little kids printed on it – you had to look quite hard because the pictures were hidden by the brown colour. There were lots of little kids and they were holding hands and standing all around the hem of my dress. (Say 'children' said my mam but I never did.) Then Mam made me a little hanky to match and I could push it up the sleeve of the cardy she was going to knit. She knitted me a light brown cardigan to go with my new dress. Well, I called it light brown but Mam said it was beige. On the knitting pattern, there were lovely little girl dancers, all dancing in a circle and they would go with my dress even more. Mam said that these were special dancers – they were ballet dancers and I liked them, but the special dancers never got knitted into my cardy. You see, Mam said that the pattern looked complicated and she hadn't got time to do anything fiddly. We had just got some new hens and it was her job to look after them and even though I locked them up at night for her she had a lot of other things to do as well – so no ballet dancers for me. Anyway, I had some new knickers, we bought them from Hull when I went to hospital for my check-up. They ballooned out a bit because they were next size up so I could grow into them, Mam said. At last everything was ready for my first day at school.

On the morning of my first day I had to get a good wash before I could put my school clothes on. I had to stand in my big knickers in our wash house while Mam lathered my face with hard green soap and rubbed it dry with our rough grey towel. Then at last I could put my dress and cardy on and finally I was ready.

Our school was at Ringam and Mam took me on the bus for my first day. When we got there, we stood in a long queue of new kids at my classroom door. Mam and me stood waiting and waiting to meet my teacher, we were outside and I was glad of my new cardy to keep me warm. Every now and again we shuffled forwards. Mam couldn't really spare this time she always had so much work to do on our farm and in our house.

The teacher took ages with each kid. I could hear her talking in a high singsong voice. Then at last it was my turn and I stood there in front of her, Mam started to tell her that I had been very poorly as a little baby and that I was not very strong yet.

"She has been very poorly she …"

"Oh, she'll be fine with us, goodbye, Mummy." And she scooted me in front of her class. There were rows of staring faces. I'd never seen so many kids before. In fact, I'd never seen any kids who were my age.

"Now, class, this is another new little girl," she said. And then she turned to me. "Now tell me who you want to sit near — who do you know?" Well I didn't know anybody. I had never seen any of them before. I knew our Gwendy and Terry of course but they were in another class. Our Katy was at the big school in Ripsea. So, there was nobody in this room that I knew so I didn't answer.

"Never mind, my dear, here's a nice little girl called Brenda and she didn't know anybody either when she came to school."

Brenda smiled at me. She was dressed in a grey jumper and skirt. I sat down on the bench next to her and my teacher went off for another new kid.

We had 'Letters of the alphabet' lesson first. Everybody shouted out when my teacher pointed at a picture with her stick. I had never heard of the alphabet but there was 'Eh' for egg and I liked that one. Our hens laid eggs so I knew about eggs. Every hen we had laid one egg a day and we collected them — hundreds of them in baskets and we would have even more now we had got some new hens. Oops! Hold on — they were all on 'Fu' for fox now, you had to blow through your teeth and not make a sound just like a fox at night when it's coming to get your hens. Now we were up to 'Hu' for hen, I knew all about hens of course. Every night I went round all our hen huts in our fields and made sure they were safe. I had to close the pop holes to keep the fox away from the hens. We must never forget the fox.

I knew a lot about eggs and hens and foxes and now I was quite excited waiting to tell everybody all about them when my teacher asked. Then she would say in her high singsong voice 'You are good at eggs and hens and foxes' and then I could put it on my 'What I am good at' list. But she never asked and she just kept on going with the alphabet lesson till they got to the end.

Then it was playtime. I ran out into the playground and jumped and shouted at the top of my voice. Then a lad pushed me from behind and I turned round and gave him a great shove

39

back. Then he said that he was going to 'tell' and our teacher came out and he 'told'. He was like a fox that lad, just waiting to get you when your back was turned.

"I thought your mummy said that you were a poorly little girl – you don't seem like it to me, running about and hurting people like that," shouted my teacher in a voice that was not singsong now – it was a low big bellow like our bull when we teased him. She made me stand near some sinks in our cloakroom. I stood there miserably and watched the drip, drip of a tap.

Then after a bit my teacher said I had to go out again because playtime had ended and I had to do the drill with everybody else. She blew a whistle and we had 'How to get back into our classroom' lesson. First, we had to line up sideways. Then we had to put our right hand on the next person's shoulder and stand there till my teacher's whistle blew again. Every time that whistle blew you had to do something that my teacher shouted at you.

"Arms down." Whistle.

"Jump turn." Whistle.

"Forward march." Whistle.

"Left, right." Whistle, whistle, and we all had to swing our arms and go back in to our classroom. I was doing it alright till Brenda turned and looked at me and we started to laugh so we didn't do it properly after that and we could hardly walk into our classroom because of laughing – I was no good at drill.

"Now, who has been good? Who am I going to choose to give our baby dolly a bath?" sing-songed my teacher and she held up a baby doll dressed in white clothes. All us girls and some boys folded their arms and held them high up on their stuck-out chests. But that lad called Charley Fox who had told on me, just grinned and didn't fold his arms at all. Then all the others breathed in and held their breaths and stuck their chests out even more – even Brenda did it so I copied, hoping I would be chosen.

"I'm not going to choose you," my teacher said to me even though I was sticking my chest out better than anybody else. "You have not been good, so I won't choose you. Now, let me see," said my teacher looking round her class.

"I think I am going to choose... Helen. Yes, Helen King you have been a good little girl you can wash the baby dolly. Come out to the front."

And when Helen went to the front I knew why she had been chosen. She looked so pretty in her pink dress, her fair hair hung in gentle curls and her skin was smooth and white and thin like a hen's eggshell. She stood there with her hands together in front of her, looking so lovely anybody would have chosen her instead of me.

"Now, which special little friend do you want to help you, Helen?" sing-songed my teacher. She would surely never choose me. I was right, she didn't choose me and she couldn't see anybody else she wanted either so off she went on her own to that sink where I had been told to stand at playtime because I was not good. Oh, how I hated that sink then but how I would have loved to be there now as Helen's special little friend washing that baby doll with soft white soap and drying it on a cuddly fluffy towel.

At dinnertime, we all went into our playground again but this time there was an old lady with us. She was called Miss Kenny and she had to take us to Ringam village hall where we had to eat our dinner. Miss Kenny wore a beige raincoat the same colour as my cardy and a brown felt hat with a strap under her chin like a basket upside down and she carried a basket, like her hat but the right way up of course. All the kids called it 'lucky basket' because they said she kept goodies in there for some lucky kids. After dinner, we played in our playground. I didn't forget that foxy lad though in case he got me when I had my back turned.

We had 'Handkerchief' lesson in the afternoon. My teacher said, "Now, children, when I tap on the desk I want you to get your handkerchiefs out." She banged on her desk and everybody

41

shifted about and fumbled in their pockets. I felt up my beige cardy sleeve and found my little brown hanky that Mam had made me. I watched everybody put their hankies out in front. I could see Helen's hanky and it was pure white with pink lace all round. Brenda's hanky was a grey square. Charley Fox hadn't got a hanky.

"Now, children, when I tap again I want you to hold your handkerchief up high above your heads."

'Bang' – they all lifted their hankies high up like flags and I did the same. I wasn't in trouble this time, it was Charley's turn. He was in trouble because he hadn't got a hanky.

"Charley Fox, if I have told you once I have told you a hundred times you must have a handkerchief in school," said our teacher in her big bull bellow voice and she gave him a bit of brown paper to use when his nose dripped.

At the end of the day we had story time and I loved it, this was the best part about coming to school. Our teacher read to us, nobody ever had any time to read to me at our house Anyway it was a story about Belle of the Ballet. It was Helen's storybook and she had kindly lent it to our teacher so we could all hear it. I am very glad she did. It was about a girl who was a good ballet dancer and she was very good at her lessons and I kept thinking that I was Belle. Oh! I could have listened forever and I couldn't help wishing that Mam had been able to knit those ballet dancers round my cardy.

At going home time I went down to our bus stop holding hands with Brenda and we sat on our bus together. She told me she lived on a little farm in a village called Sunkstead but it came after Gum so I got off the bus before her. I tore down our lane with our Gwendy and we burst through our door and Mam brought us lovely eggs on toast for tea.

I got quite friendly with Brenda after that and she was my special friend now and we used to go to each other's houses to play at weekends. When I stayed overnight at her house I asked our Gwendy to drop the pop hole to keep our hens safe at night. I didn't forget the fox.

I got off the bus at Brenda's lane end and she was always there waiting with her big sister Jeany with their horse and trap. Their horse was not like our old Dobbin, of course, because this horse wasn't a cart horse. He had been a racehorse but had retired now and he was called Lucky Basket, which Dad said was a sort of swear word but I didn't understand that. We all called Miss Kenny's basket 'lucky basket' and that wasn't a swear word but Dad said that was different.

Anyway, Brenda jumped down and ran to meet me and we did our joke about 'arms down, jump turn, forward march' and we shouted it at the top of our voices and did actions laughing our heads off. Then we got into the little high cart – it was only meant for two people but we squashed up together and Jeany said, "Walk on, Lucky Basket," and he stepped out left, right daintily down their lane to their house.

Brenda and me played about all day on their farm. Sometimes I was allowed to milk their cow. You see, they didn't have a big herd like us and they didn't have milking machines because they only had one cow and they milked her by hand. She was called Buttercup because she lived in a field full of bright yellow buttercups and they didn't care what letter the people were on down south. They just called her what they wanted. I had a try at milking Buttercup but I hardly got any milk and we all laughed. Then Brenda squirted the milk really well and it rattled into the bucket and frothed up into creamy bubbles. For tea, we had rabbit pie with a rabbit shot from their field by Brenda's Dad and apple pie, with apples from their orchard, for pudding.

At night, I slept in a bed with Brenda and Jeany. One night her mam and dad had gone out and I was a bit frightened so I cuddled up under the blankets and Jeany went down to their kitchen to get something to cheer me up. Brenda stroked my arm while we were waiting. Jeany brought us some of Buttercup's milk in a big enamel mug and cocoa powder mixed with sugar on an old plate. We sucked our fingers to make them wet and then dipped them in the mixture. It was crunchy and sweet and bitter all at the same time and it was the best thing I had ever tasted. Then we passed round the mug of Buttercup's milk and we all had a drink. I fell asleep with Jeany on one side of me and Brenda on the other.

Next day, when it was time to go home, Jeany got Lucky Basket ready. Then Brenda and me did 'arms down, jump turn forward march' and laughed our heads off as we marched up to Lucky Basket and jumped into his little trap. Then off we went stepping out left, right, back up their road in time for me to catch my bus home. Then on Monday it was school again.

School went on the same as it always had – Helen always knew the answers and was good at everything and I hadn't found anything at school that I was good at yet. But I had found Brenda.

Then one day we were playing outside at dinnertime and that rough lad Charley Fox started pushing Helen from behind – just like he did to me that time. Well, Helen didn't know what to do because she usually just kept to herself. She often stayed in doing jobs for the teacher or she just hugged that baby doll near Miss Kenny. But this time she was caught on her own so Charley kept on pushing her till she was in tears, she was helpless and he was just laughing.

"I'm going to get Miss Kenny," shouted Brenda and she ran for help at top speed off round the corner where Miss Kenny was holding one end of a big skipping rope while a girl held the other end. Some girls were jumping up and down when the rope went round.

"Oh do go away," I heard Helen cry. "Please do stop it." But it was no use you can't ask a lad like that to stop teasing you he'll do it even more. You can't ask a fox to stop getting hens. He will just go for them it's his nature and the only way you can stop him is to keep the hens out of his way. I knew that, but Helen didn't so I ran over to where Charley was pushing her. She had given up and her head was down on her chest and her arms wrapped round her folded body. Charley was in for the kill. Miss Kenny hadn't come yet so I had to do something fast.

"Hey," I shouted at Charley, "leave her alone." And then I shouted to Helen, "Run away, Helen, run." But she just stood there in a daze. I've seen hens do that when a fox chases them. They sometimes just freeze with fright. But I knew what would happen next, the fox would come in and bite their heads off. Helen didn't know this so I gave her a push and screamed louder, "Go on run away," and this time she ran and ran on her dainty little sandaled feet with her blonde hair streaming behind her. Then I turned to Charley and gave him such a big shove that he fell over. I knew I would be in trouble again and I knew that I would have to stand near that sink with its dripping tap. Charley lay on the hard playground floor.

"Now what's going on here?" my teacher shouted in her bull bellow voice. She must have heard all the fuss and rushed out. She looked at me with a frown.

"She punched me," shouted Charley pointing at me and wiping his nose on his sleeve – he must have lost his bit of brown paper.

"Is that true?" asked teacher. But before I could answer Miss Kenny was there holding Brenda's hand and she spoke up straight away. "He was hitting Helen and he must have fallen over when he was chasing her," said Miss Kenny firmly. I don't know what she saw but that's what she said.

"Charley, go and stand in the cloakroom for hitting Helen," said our teacher in her low bellow voice. It was his turn to stand by the dripping tap.

"You got away with that, you're a lucky b..." whispered Charley to me as he went.

Not long after that Helen invited me to her house for a night. I suppose it was because I had helped her but I could hardly believe it, *me* to go to the posh Helen King's house? I was supposed to be going to Brenda's but going to her house was ordinary compared to going to Helen's house. There was no competition so I told Brenda I was going to the Kings' house and she just nodded and smiled a little smile.

45

And Mam smiled a very big smile when I told her about my invitation. She was very pleased and she said that I would get on in the world and better myself if I mixed with posh people like the Kings. So, there you are, I didn't need my 'What I am good at' list I just needed to have Helen as my special friend. I closed my list in my head and I didn't need to think about it ever again. I was a bit sad because it was like saying goodbye to an old friend but I had got a new and more important one.

Mam started getting me ready very early on Saturday morning. First I had to learn how to speak properly. You see, Helen lived in Ringam but now Mam said that was not its real name. It turned out that we had always shortened it and I had to learn to say its proper name which was High Ringham. I was very nervous and I was sure I wouldn't remember to say it properly. Mam never mentioned that we had always shortened Gumbalding to Gum – but maybe that didn't matter as much as posh High Ringham.

Of course, to go to the Kings' house I had to get a good scrub down in our wash house with our hard, green soap and rough towel again. I wore my brown school dress with little kids on, my beige cardy and my school knickers, which fitted me now not because I had grown but they had shrunk in the wash. Then I got on the bus at our lane end.

Mr King was in his car waiting at the bus stop when I got off. It was a big car with soft seats and you couldn't feel any bumps in the road as we went along but I knew they were there because you could feel them rattling when you were in our car.

When we got to Helen's I could see that everything there was much smarter than at Brenda's. For a start, we had tea in china cups not mugs and then 'Mummy' came in pushing a trolley with silver dishes and silver knives and forks.

"Please take us as you find us," she said. "We don't stand on ceremony here." Well it was a ceremony to me with a feast fit for a King. After a salad and cooked ham, we had trifle with all sorts of layers, I just can't tell you what was in there what with all that jelly and fruit and cream and custard. I was so happy

46

that I tried to have a joke with them about the drill at school and I started laughing 'Arms down...' but I didn't carry on because Mr King interrupted lifting his right hand, then he said that such discipline was a good idea. I didn't say any more and just sat looking at books in the afternoon.

We were going to a concert after tea and Helen was going to dance in it. Mr King rang for a taxi – we were going to a theatre in style. Just imagine if we were at Brenda's we would be going squashed up in old Lucky Basket's trap but now because I was going with very important people I was going in a taxi. The taxi came all the way from Hull.

We went to a big hall and I sat down with Mr and Mrs King. Then after a long time the lights went off and the show got going. There were people singing and dancing on stage in big flowing dresses and dark suits. I had never seen anything like it before and it lasted for ages and we weren't allowed to move or talk. I must say I didn't like it much. Then at last Helen came on. She was dressed in a pink fluffy dress that was short and sticking out as if her mummy had been very busy with starch. You could see her pink knickers as well and they were made of lace, layers and layers of it. Then she started to dance, she pointed her little pink toes and lifted her arching arms over her head. She did little twirls and little jumps then up and up she sailed then she sailed down and down, over and over again. She was just like Belle of the Ballet and I realised that I would never be. Then it was all over and they were all clapping and Helen did a curtsey. Then the lights came on and we went back to Ringam ('Say High Ringham,' said my mam but I couldn't get used to it so I never did).

Back at Helen's house we didn't talk and laugh, in fact I didn't see Helen again that night, instead her mummy showed me to a guest bedroom. There was a little dressing table with pink flowery material round and a little bedspread with matching pink and matching patterns. I had never seen such a room and when I lifted the blankets I saw flat smooth sheets as white as Helen's hanky. I kept my knickers on just to be on the safe side as I slid in between the sheets. Then suddenly I started to cry, my tears came thick and fast just pouring down my face. You see, I had never been on my own in a bedroom at night like this. My sisters had always slept in our bedroom with me and when I was at Brenda's I slept with her and her sister Jeany, in one bed, so there was always somebody there if you needed them. But here there was nobody. Oh, how I longed for Jeany's bitter sweet cocoa and sugar mixture that tasted better than any trifle ever could. And oh, how I wished that Brenda was here to stroke my arm. Then I saw a glass of cold water on my bedside table and to try and stop my tears I took a gulp, but it was nowhere near as nice as the creamy bubbly milk Jeany had brought me from Buttercup. My tears kept coming and I thought that they would never stop. But then after a long, long time when I had no more tears left, I fell into a dark and lonely sleep. In the morning, I couldn't eat my breakfast and Mr King took me all the way home to Gum in his big smooth car.

I hadn't much enjoyed my visit to the Kings but I didn't say anything because I wanted get on in the world. Anyway, nobody wanted to listen. You see, I had forgotten the deadly fox and he had come in for the kill last night. I had been so excited about going to Helen's and getting on in the world that I had forgotten to ask anybody to lock up our hens at night. And of course, that cunning fox had gone into one of their huts. They must have all frozen in fear when they saw him and he tore into them. What a mess he had made. There were headless hens everywhere all strewn about with blood and feathers. My dad could not be proud of me now and Mam was disappointed. I would never ever forget the fox again but it did no good to say that then. There was no comfort for me – no Brenda to fetch Miss Kenny to take my side and stick up for me and no teacher to stand the fox near the dripping tap. I was so miserable. Maybe Helen would help me.

I told her all about it on Monday at school but she just put her hands over her ears and screamed, "Oh don't tell me about it. I don't want to think about blood." So I told Brenda and she understood and stroked my arm. This getting on in the world was not easy.

And things got even harder for me because not long after that I heard that Helen was leaving our school at the end of half-term and going to a private school where there were only posh girls. That was the end of me getting on in the world by having Helen King as my special friend.

Then after our half-term holiday there was some good news for me at last. It was in Miss Kenny's lucky basket. It was a little box for me all wrapped up in pink paper from Helen. Inside was a little charm bracelet made with a silver chain and links all round it. I had never seen anything so dainty in all my life. And there was more, because deep inside the paper I found a little ballet dancer charm in a pink dress. When I got home I clipped her onto the charm bracelet and then I had an idea and went to get my farthing that Great Aunty Dilly had given me. I remembered it had a little ring on and it fastened easily onto my chain. I put my bracelet on my arm and when I moved the little ballet dancer dangled and danced round the little brown wren. I was cheered up already.

And to cheer myself up even more I brought my 'What I am good at' list back and I was sure to get loads of things on it very soon. Then at school I was so happy because Brenda still wanted me as her friend and she acted as if I had never been away and we began to talk and laugh again just like we used to. And I went to her house as often as I wanted and when I got off the bus at Sunkstead, Lucky Basket was always there waiting and Brenda always ran to meet me and we always shouted, "Arms down, jump turn, forward march." And we jumped into the little trap laughing our heads off and Lucky Basket went left, right, stepping out down the lane to their house.

It's not a boy!

Chapter 5

Aunty Cecily

Mam was always sewing; when I went to bed I could hear her machine downstairs. Even when our stair door was closed I could still hear it – rattle, rrattle it went, then rrrrrrr when it got going at top speed. Every night I heard her sewing clothes for us all from bits of material that nobody else wanted. She was always going to our remnant shop in Ripsea or unpicking old clothes. Then she laid the material on our table and cut out funny looking shapes. Then she sat at her machine concentrating, with her feet on the pedal going backwards and forwards and the needle going up and down so fast it was just a blur. And out came coats, dresses, blouses, skirts and everything you could want.

Except that all I wanted was to go to the shops in Hull and actually buy new clothes like Helen King and other posh people did. But no, Mam had to make all our clothes to save money. Every spare penny had to be spent on our farm animals and implements. Our farm was the most important thing in our lives and we all knew that because Dad said it was our livelihood. So, Mam had to make everything out of anything. She even made the mattress for my bed.

I never got big enough to come out of my cot and go into a proper bed but I did get old enough. So, one day Mam decided the time had come and she got some empty sacks out of our barn and spread them out on our table and cut the seams to make flat squares. Then she washed them and she sewed them up together on her sewing machine and made two big bags. She stuffed them full of fresh straw from bales in our stack yard and then I had a mattress. Well it was in two halves so I had two mattresses really, pushed up together, so when I went into my big bed at last, my straw mattress had a crack down the middle.

And I liked that crack because in winter when it got very cold I snuggled up and put my feet down it to warm them up. And that crack was good in another way as well because it was a safe place to keep my treasures. My little charm bracelet and its brown wren and pink ballet dancer were there and at night when I was frightened or worried I could hold them in the dark and feel safe in my bed.

One morning my dad had to get out of his bed in a hurry because a sheep was lambing with twins and she was having problems so she needed his help. Well, apparently, this sheep was heaving and straining but she couldn't get her twins out of her body. Dad had to call our vet who cut the mother sheep open and she died. But the vet pulled out two sloppy, floppy lambs and they were alive. Dad grabbed them straight away and cleared their mouths of slime. Then he got a handful of straw and started to rub them down. He rubbed on their little wet coats of curly sprouting wool till suddenly one bleated 'Maaa' and then the next one copied his brother. They were both alive and well but what could we do with two little orphan lambs?

Well there was another sheep, our only black sheep, the one that had made me laugh when I was a baby. She was getting old and her lamb had been born dead. But she was an experienced mother and Dad had a special job for her now. He wanted her to feed one little orphan lamb. But sheep won't just do that easily, you know. If their lamb dies they won't just adopt another baby and bring it up as their own like humans do. No, if another lamb comes up to her for milk that sheep will sniff at it to see if it smells like hers and then when it doesn't, she butts it away and she won't let it drink milk from her. Dad tried this cunning trick.

He got his penknife and cut the woolly coat off the dead lamb and spread it out on some straw – it was a funny shape now, like a cut-out bit of Mam's material. Then Dad tied the dead lamb's woolly shape onto one of the orphan lambs, with binder twine. The lamb looked really funny running about with its new coat on, bleating for some milk. Then our old black sheep came up to it and sniffed it and she didn't suspect a thing she just thought 'That smells like my lamb,' and she let it drink her milk. And she would bring it up as her own now and that was the end of that, but we still had the other twin with no mother.

There was nothing for it – I had to look after that little remnant of a lamb, that nobody else wanted, and bring it up as my pet lamb. Every morning before I went to school I had to feed him with the calf's milk made up from powder and water. I mixed it up in a bucket and stirred it with a stick and then put the mixture in a bottle and put a teat on and got my pet lamb to suckle that. He was really greedy and strong, my lamb – he pushed and pushed at the bottle to get more milk faster and nearly knocked it out of my hands. He grew very quickly and he just loved me. We were friends. He followed me about wherever I went and when I went to school he followed me up to the bus stop at our lane end. He waited till I got on our school bus then he ran back to our farm. Then at night when I got back he was always at the top of our lane waiting there for me. He must have worked out when I was coming back home and trotted up to meet me; he was very clever, my lamb. I couldn't wait to show him to Aunty Cecily.

Aunty Cecily wasn't my real Aunty of course – none of my aunties had such a posh name as that. But my mam said that it was only polite to call her Aunty because we could not call a grown up just by her first name – that would be rude. You must not be rude if you want to get on in the world. Aunty Cecily was a friend of Aunty Peggy's – they had met in the war when they were both working and passing on secret messages. They would be lifelong friends like my pet lamb and me.

Aunty Cecily lived down south in London and worked in a posh shop that sold very expensive materials that you bought for a dressmaker to make into clothes for you. There was no sewing up bits of scrap materials on your own sewing machine at night for Aunty Cecily's posh ladies.

Aunty Peggy brought Aunty Cecily to see us all at Gum and we stared at her fashionable clothes ('Don't stare – it's rude,' said

Mam, but we always did) and we stared even more when we were trying to understand her posh way of talking.

I took her to our paddock to see my pet lamb and she tiptoed carefully in her little satin shoes that looked as if they belonged to a ballet dancer like Helen. Then she spread her picnic rug out. She had brought it especially so she could sit on our grass. I saw her kick bits of muck away before she carefully unfolded it. The blood red tartan made our green grass jump. I could see Aunty Cecily's big curls bouncing up and down as she nodded her head and concentrated. She used to do that – nod her head, when she was being serious and she was very serious getting herself ready to sit down comfortably in our paddock. She pressed her stockinged legs together and went down sideways – very posh and ladylike. Then she watched me feed my little lamb – well, he was not so little now he was growing so fast. He grew much faster than I did in fact.

"Oh, he's such a da-ahling, isn't he? What a perfectly lovely petty lamb," she said in her posh voice. My mam thought that Aunty Cecily was a good person to have around because she was from down south where you got on in the world. We kids might copy her posh way of talking to help us better ourselves, Mam thought, but we never did.

Anyway, Aunty Cecily couldn't have been all that good because she didn't know anything about farms.

"Oh, look at those da-ahling ewes in the meadow," she said looking at our mother sheep in our paddock.

"They are called sheep and they are in our paddock," I said surprised at her not knowing but she just looked at me from the top of her eyes with her head nodding a bit. I knew she would think I was rude but I had never heard of a ewe and we never called our fields meadows. I was surprised that Aunty Cecily did not know that.

She certainly didn't know about farms but as I've said she knew about fashion did Aunty Cecily. I stared at her lovely red coat which matched the colour of her rug and my eyes jumped at the bright colour when I looked at it.

"I love your coat, Aunty Cecily, and I like that woolly collar – it's just like Mam's hair when she's had a perm." Mam's black, perm curls were tight and hard not like Aunty Cecily's which were light brown and soft and fashionable.

"Da-ahling, it's an astrakhan collar. The wool comes from special lambs abroad."

"Do lambs have to be killed to make your collar?"

"Da-ahling, I imagine so but I do not like to think about that. I just like to think about the fashion."

"But I expect they had to be killed and skinned," I went on.

"Oh please – I do not want to think about that, it's perfectly horrid thinking about anything hurting da-ahling lambs, let's change the subject, shall we?" Her head was nodding quite a lot now and her big curls were bouncing up and down.

"What is the name of your petty lamb?" Well I hadn't really thought of it – I just called him pet lamb.

"I know, da-ahling, let's call him Astrakhan – that's a very fitting name – yes Astrakhan it is." I wasn't keen I can tell you because she was supposed to be changing the subject but we were still really talking about those little lambs from another country that had to be killed and skinned to make collars. But I didn't say anything; I didn't want to risk being rude again. Mam would not like it.

"Right that's settled then and now – why don't we ask your mummy to buy you a new coat if you like mine so much?"

I hadn't grown out of my old one and you can't just ask for new things, not when there were animals to be fed and implements to be kept in good running order. The farm was our livelihood. But Aunty Cecily didn't seem to know this. I told you she didn't know much about farms.

"My mam always makes my coat," I said with a shrug. My mam used her own old coat and unpicked it and turned it inside out before cutting out the shapes to make a new coat for me. Just like that little orphan lamb, I had to wear somebody else's coat. But oh, how I would have loved to go to the shop for a really fashionable one in Hull.

Aunty Cecily smiled and looked again at me from the top of her eyes and her head nodded quite fast.

She jumped up with her legs still pressed together and shook bits of grass off her rug.

"Let's see what Mummy says," she said tiptoeing off as best she could, trying not to dirty her satin shoes. I knew what Mam would say. We never bought any clothes from shops except knickers.

Asty (I decided Asty was alright as a name, so long as I didn't think of Astrakhan) ran after us bleating for some more milk. He was a greedy little lamb because you could see he had had enough to eat. His fat stomach was sticking out like a big round barrel. But he must have thought it was always worth asking. We shut the gate on him but he nipped through a gap in the hedge and was right behind us when we got to our house door. Aunty Cecily looked sternly at Asty through the top of her eyes but it made no difference, he still followed. She shut our house door carefully but when we got inside we could hear an awful banging and scraping.

"Oh da-ahling, what is that dreadful noise?"

"It's Astrakhan banging on our door for some more food. Take no notice, he knows the answer is no." I thought I'd better give him his full name while she was around so as not to be rude because Mam was there.

"Mummy, your da-ahing little girl would really like a new and fashionable coat, like mine," said Aunty Cecily turning her attention to more important matters with her head nodding a bit and her curls gently bobbing up and down.

"I haven't time to make a new coat," said Mam pedalling away at her sewing machine. She was making a work shirt for Dad.

"Well, I wouldn't mind one from a posh shop in Hull," I said, it was always worth asking like Asty did even though we both knew what answer would be.

"You know we haven't got money for that, the farm comes first," Mam said and even Aunty Cecily, staring hard at Mam out of the top of her eyes and nodding her head so furiously that her big curls nearly rolled away, made no difference. I knew what the answer would be. My mam pressed the pedal and her machine went off at top speed making such a noise that she wouldn't hear us if we asked again. In the end, Aunty Cecily gave up and went back home down south to London.

Then a few weeks after she had gone and we had all forgotten about her, Posty came riding on his bike wobbling all over our lane, with a big heavy parcel on the handlebars. He staggered with it into our backyard and handed it over to Mam. Asty came running up and gave him a big butt for his troubles. My lamb was getting very strong now and butted everybody except me. No, he never butted me. I was his lifelong friend. He followed me everywhere and he was always trying to get more food from me even though he was quite big enough to feed himself by now. There was plenty of grass in our paddock and sheep meal in the troughs. But he kept on nuzzling my hand and he was too old for milk now so I started to carry a few oats in my coat pocket to give to him. So of course, he followed me even more.

Anyway, back to that parcel, the postmark said 'London' and for a little minute, I did think that it might be a new coat for me with a fashionable astrakhan collar. I tried not to think about that special little lamb from abroad that would have to give up his life for the collar.

Mam tore open the parcel on our big wooden table and we all stood round. It wasn't often that a parcel came for us (well never really). I stood there hoping against hope for my new coat.

It wasn't a coat for me. It was hundreds of lengths of material form Aunty Cecily's workplace. They were samples of material from her shop – much bigger and better than our old

Ripsea remnants. They were last year's fashion but last year's fashion down south hadn't got to us yet and I forgot about my coat as I just stared in disbelief at that parcel full of treasure. There were embroidered flowers, little Bo Peep prints, stripes and bold bright shapes of all kinds. There were silks and satins and cotton, rough and smooth in more colours than the rainbow. We all pushed forward to grab our favourite pieces and hold them up against our shabby dresses. Soon there was material all over our room. We liked this best, then changed our minds and liked that more, you just couldn't decide. But one of my favourites was Bo Peep in her beautiful long dress looking out for her sheep.

Mam sat down at her sewing machine there and then and it was unheard of for her to sew in the morning, when she should have been working on our farm. But she just couldn't wait and soon the machine was rattling away and she was stitching material together in top gear rrrrrr. Skirts and frocks flew out from under her needle and after that came a patchwork quilt for me. Oh, it was beautiful and just what I needed on a cold night. Mam filled it with sheep's wool. I couldn't believe how soon it was on my bed and I was holding rough bits and smoothing shiny bits of material between my fingers all night long. But best of all was Bo Peep in that corner over there looking for her sheep.

Then one night soon after the parcel had arrived Mam and Dad took my two sisters to Ringam to see Aunty Peggy at Sunnyside. I didn't want to go because I couldn't wait to snuggle down under my new quilt. I went to bed and waited for them to come back.

But they didn't come back and soon it got darker and darker and I got more and more frightened. I got out of bed and stood on our bedroom windowsill to look for our car lights. Whenever our car came home in the dark its headlights beamed round our walls. But no lights came.

Grandma was next door and Mam always said, 'In an emergency bang on fire back with our poker.' Grandma's fire was back to back with ours and she always sat on a chair by her fire so she would hear me banging and come and help me. But it wasn't an emergency, was it? I wasn't poorly and they would surely come back before long. Wouldn't they? I stood on the sill and waited.

Soon I was freezing cold and I had to go back to bed to get warm and tuck my feet in my mattress crack. I looked over the top of my quilt again to see if our car lights were beaming round our wall but there was nothing just darkness. They didn't come back.

I was very scared now. What if they never came back? I went under my quilt and put my hands down under the sheet and in the crack to get my charm bracelet and put it on. I felt a bit safer. It was then I heard a banging noise.

I stayed very still and listened again but then there was nothing. I must have imagined it. Bang. Bang. There it was again. Was this an emergency? Should I creep down and knock on the fire back to get Grandma? I could feel the little ballet dancer and wren dancing round my wrist. Then there was silence and I was safe again

But the noise came back. Bang, bang. And then there was a scraping. This had to be an emergency now. I had better go and knock for Grandma. I knew now that there was nothing for it but to get help.

I crept downstairs and through our stair door and down our passage where my bare feet felt the shock of our cold stone floor. All I had to do was go down our passage and into our room where I could get the poker and bang on the fire back. But as I was going past our outside door there was a draft coming in, a very cold draft. Mam must not have shut our door properly. Stiff with fear I shuffled on and it was then I tripped and fell with a scream, down onto a soft woolly body.

'Baa, baa.' It was only Asty, thank goodness. I buried my face in his woolly belly and smelt his warm lamb smell.

"What are you doing here? It's the middle of the night," I said in a cross voice but I can tell you I was pleased he was with me and I sat down on the floor and talked to him in the dark. Asty must have kicked our door open. I went and fetched some oats out of my coat pocket and he got what he had wanted after all. He ate greedily.

It was then I taught Asty his first trick, just there and then on our cold stone floor in the dark that night. And suddenly it was as if all the darkness had gone and even though the headlights hadn't even beamed on our wall I forgot all about our car coming back as I concentrated on Asty.

Every time he did his trick right, I gave him some food as a reward. All he had to do was to hold his leg up to shake hands like some dogs do and then I'd give him more oats. He learnt it in a flash because he was a very clever lamb. We practised for a bit then suddenly there were our car lights beaming across our wall. Quick as a flash I pushed Asty outside, closed the door and darted back upstairs, jumped into bed and pretended to be asleep and that wasn't hard to do because I nodded off straight away dreaming of teaching Asty some more tricks.

In the morning, Mam told me that she had been talking to Aunty Peggy about our parcel of material from Aunty Cecily and that she lost all track of time. So, everything was alright and I taught Asty even more tricks. He learnt very quickly. He could 'stay' when I went away and then come running when I clapped my hands. He could jump over a little gate when I shouted 'jump' and I set up a little obstacle course for him in our orchard and we practised every day. He could even hide and then come running when I shouted for him. I was a very good trainer and I thought that one day I might be able to take Asty round our villages and show everybody how he performed. I even put – teaching my pet lamb to do tricks – on my 'What I am good at' list. But I never did get to take Asty round our villages to show my performing lamb because something awful happened.

You see, one day I got off our school bus and Asty wasn't there waiting for me like he usually was.

'That's funny,' I thought. 'He was here this morning to see me off to school.' I felt for some oats in my old coat pocket and shouted, "Asty, Asty." But I got all the way down our lane to our house and my lamb didn't come to me. I looked in his paddock but he was not there. 'Oh,' I thought, 'maybe he's just doing one of his hiding tricks.' But when I clapped my hands he still didn't come and I was really worried. Mam was calling me in for tea and I still hadn'tt seen Asty. I was getting frantic but to calm myself I remembered that last time I was worried there was a perfectly good explanation and everything was soon alright again.

But everything wasn't alright this time.

"I can't find Asty, Mam, have you seen him?" I asked when I sat down for tea.

"Oh, your dad took him to market today and sold him," she said serving lamb chops and onions with thick gravy on my plate. A warm lamb smell came up to my nose.

"What? You sold Asty, my lifelong friend?"

"Yes, you know that all lambs go to market; we can't afford to keep them for ever. The farm is our livelihood you know and besides that, he was getting very rough butting Posty and everybody."

"But Asty… at Hull market… he'll be killed."

'He's for the chop, he's for the chop,' Posty could shout round all our villages. It should have been me going round with my pet lamb showing everybody how clever he was and what a good trainer I was.

"This will cheer you up," smiled Mam. "Your lamb was so big and fat that he made a good price at market and your dad said you can have some of the money to buy a new coat from a shop in Hull – so you have got what you wanted after all."

I could have a new coat from a shop in Hull instead of my lifelong friend.

I ran upstairs leaving my chop and gravy to go cold and lay in my bed and stared hopelessly at little Bo Peep without her sheep. I reached down my crack to get my bracelet but it was no comfort this time. The night came – it got darker and darker and now Asty had gone and no lights would ever shine in the darkness again. My friend had gone for ever and he would never come back. I couldn't live another day.

I did live another day of course and daylight did come – it always does. Then when winter came round again and I was getting really cold in my old threadbare coat, Mam and me went into Hull to get me a new coat. This was what I had always wanted – to buy a new coat from a shop at last. But I kept thinking of Asty and me going round our village doing our little tricks. I could have a new coat but it cost my lamb his life.

Of course, I was so sad that I just couldn't choose and so in the end Mam decided for me – my new coat was the colour of Aunty Cecily's, and my eyes jumped at the blood red and I blinked fiercely as I put it on. Thank goodness it didn't have an astrakhan collar – it had a velvet one instead.

That night I lay in bed listening to Mam's sewing machine rattle, rrattle and then it got up to top speed, rrrrr it went. Now I just knew now that when it was my turn again to have a coat or any clothes made by Mam from scraps of old material I would not mind one little bit.

Chapter 6

The Beautiful Rose

It wasn't long before I got a new friend – not that I would ever forget my pet lamb of course and nothing could ever make up for him being taken away from me to go to Hull market. But I did find a very different sort of friend on our farm.

The first I knew of him was when I heard him breathing. I was playing in our stack yard on my own one day.

"Ah, aah." I could hear somebody behind our straw stack and I tiptoed to the edge and peeped round.

It was a tramp and he was just like a bundle of black rags slumped against our yellow bales. He looked so ugly in his dirty torn clothes and his old cracked boots. His cap seemed to grow from his head, with bits of black hair sprouting through it. I watched him and listened to his breathing in secret hardly daring to breathe myself in case he heard me. But then I coughed by accident and the tramp bundle moved and I could see his black darting eyes. I jumped back but it was too late.

"Hello, my beauty." He smiled at me and the skin on his face cracked into old leather like his boots and I could see big gaps (even bigger than mine) in his bad teeth. I wasn't sure that I should go near him but he kept on smiling and then he beckoned me over with his grubby hand. Gradually I crept round our bales and stood in front of him in the straw. He smiled again and said, "Nice to see you, my beauty." I didn't know what to do as I watched him chewing on nothing and licking his dry lips then I had an idea. I ran off to our pantry and got some cheese and put it between two slices of bread then I got a mug of water and ran back to our stack yard. As I ran some water spilled and slapped down my dress and as I gripped the sammy ('Say sandwich,' said my mam but I always forgot to), my fingers sank into the soft bread making it mushy – it was all a mess. But when I got back to my tramp you would have thought that I had brought him a feast. His eyes lit up and his face cracked into an even bigger smile than when he first saw me. He glugged the water down then he held the squashed doughy lump up to his mouth and in a flash, it was gone. I sat down in the straw hoping he would talk but he just smiled gently at me and fell asleep, so I crept away. After that he slept in our bales every night. During the day, he went tramping the roads to find a bit of casual work in exchange for some food; he called it meat for work. Then he came back to sleep in our straw and he was always so pleased to see me. He told me about his day and the bits of work he had been doing and I used to tell him what had happened to me. He listened very carefully and smiled at me all the time when it was my turn to talk.

I didn't tell anybody about my new friend because I was sure that Mam would think a tramp was not a good friend to have. You see, she would think that he could not help me get on in the world, to do that she thought that your clothes had to be smart and you certainly had to be clean and speak properly. Mam wanted me to mix with people like Helen or Aunty Cecily who had all the things that she thought I needed. My tramp was not at all like them so I kept quiet. Nowadays I was secretly relying on my list of things that I was good at to get me on in the world, so it didn't matter to me that my friend was dirty. And as I got to know him it was funny, but I didn't think he was ugly any more. I didn't bother about his old dirty clothes. All I looked for was his kindly smile and I liked how he listened to what I told him. He was as good a friend to me as my pet lamb had been and that was what I had wanted. Then one day not long after finding my tramp I got something else I wanted.

You see, Ireney asked me to be her bridesmaid. I had always longed to be a bridesmaid; it would be so exciting. Mam would be making my dress of course and I didn't mind not going to the shops to buy clothes now because I had learnt my lesson when my pet lamb had to be killed to pay for my red coat. I decided I would never grumble about Mam making me things on her sewing machine ever again.

Mam knew Ireney from Ringam and we didn't have to call her Aunty like we had to with Aunty Cecily – maybe it was because she wasn't posh. Her hair was permed into tight frizzy curls like Mam's, not soft big curls like Aunty Cecily's. And her gums showed bright red when she smiled. And another thing was that her teeth stuck out and her lips had to go all tight and thin when she closed her mouth. Ireney was not beautiful.

Maybe Ireney chose me for her bridesmaid because I wasn't beautiful either. For one thing, I had that gap in my front teeth, which was so big I could fit my Aunty Dilly's farthing up inside it and another thing was that my hair was very thin because of being poisoned when I was a baby.

Anyway, it wasn't long after I knew about being a bridesmaid that Ireney came to talk to Mam about the Big Day. They couldn't stop discussing materials and headdresses and flowers. And I couldn't stop thinking that it could be my very own Big Day.

And to make it my Big Day I had to look good. In fact, I decided I had to look beautiful and it was there and then that I promised myself that I would be the most beautiful person at the wedding. I could add that to my 'What I am good at' list. I would be good at being beautiful, but I knew that there was a lot of work to be done to make me into a beauty.

First there was my dress – Mam had, of course, used up all Aunty Cecily's lovely fabrics from London – in fact she had used them in about a week after they arrived. So there was nothing for it but to go to Ripsea to the remnant shop.

All three of us went, Ireney, Mam and me, on the bus, but when we got there I was disappointed because they started looking for material for Irene's dress first. She was going to make her own dress out of white material. At least that was one good thing. Ireney wasn't going to wear brown like Aunty Peggy did.

It's not a boy!

They turned the shop upside down and they were ages but at last they found some white silk which Mam said would look good. So, that was finally decided on and then I hoped to look for my material because I was getting fed up – but no – it was Mam's turn next and they started looking for some material for her costume – in the end she chose some navy blue which was a bargain because it turned out to be linen. She always chose navy blue; it must have been her favourite colour. At last it was my turn but we were all tired by now and the scraps and rolls of material were all over the shop and the assistant had gone into the back to get a mug of tea. I ended up with some ordinary blue which Mam said she could make into a nice dress. I must say I was a bit disappointed. I had imagined I would have silk like Ireney or linen like Mam but no, mine was just ordinary cotton. So that was the end of that and we went back home on the bus. Ireney got off at Ringam and we went on to our lane end at Gum. I was hoping that Mam would start to make my dress straight away. But when we got back she changed into her old clothes and went out to help Dad with the milking because he had already brought our cows up from Bottom Field. My material was just dumped in its brown carrier bag on our stone floor.

Then, when I got to bed I heard Mam's sewing machine start up – rattle, rrattle it went, it got into top speed and off it went rrrrr. I listened hoping that it was my dress she was making and not her costume. I didn't want her to do mine last because she might get fed up and just rush any old thing off and I had been last for the material so it would only be fair if I was first for the dress. And it was important that I had a lovely dress if I was going to look beautiful. I put my hand in my mattress crack and brought out my lucky charm bracelet and fitted my farthing in between my front teeth. It felt cold and comforting on my gum. I fell asleep to dream of being very beautiful indeed.

Next day I couldn't wait to see if Mam had been able to make my ordinary cotton into a lovely dress to make me beautiful. The first thing I did was look in her wardrobe.

Mothballs rolled out as I scrabbled in her skirts and dresses and old costumes – she had made them all from remnants and then suddenly there it was – my dress hanging right next to Dad's best black suit. She had made my dress first, and she had worked hard and it did look lovely – it even had frills round the neck and frills down the bodice. I was very pleased. There was still a long way to go before I would look beautiful but Mam had given me a good start with this dress and guess what? It was going to be long – I had never had a long dress before and it would nearly touch my shoes.

My shoes – oh, I had only just thought of them – I had no nice shoes. On our farm, I wore my wellies and they were no good for a bridesmaid, of course. And then I had my school shoes – those lace-ups that Dad brought home every year from our cobblers at Ringam. They would be no good for a bridesmaid either. I bet nobody had thought about my shoes and I was worried.

But I needn't have worried because next week Mam and me were on our bus again but this time we were not going to Ripsea we were going in the opposite direction to Hull. I was going for another hospital check-up again and Mam said that we could get some special bridesmaid shoes while we were in Hull. As you know we didn't buy clothes from shops (except knickers) – and my red coat, of course, which I don't even want to think about.

I had never ever been into a shoe shop to choose my shoes because, as I've said, Dad just brought them for us kids from our cobblers. We tried them on at home and stood on a page of Uncle Sid's *Hull Daily Mail* to keep them clean. If they didn't seem to fit Dad took them back when he went to Ringam again and got the next size up.

Going into a shoe shop was all new to me. There were white boxes lined all around the walls and we sat down on a chair. Then out came a smart lady in high heeled shoes tiptoeing all over the shop as she brought shoes for me to try.

"Try navy ones, they are serviceable and won't show the dirt," said Mam and I was disappointed she had said that because I had been hoping for some little satin slippers like Aunty Cecily wore.

"We have these, madam, which are in fashion." Mam looked impressed. And I must say that when I got them on I liked them – they had a little pattern of petals on the front and you could see my white socks through the petal holes. But then Mam saw the price and I had to take them off because they were too dear.

I sat there swinging my feet in my socks hoping that Mam would afford something that would make me look beautiful. I just hoped that she wouldn't decide I had to go in my lace-up school shoes after all.

"Have you anything cheaper?" asked Mam.

"Not in that range, madam," and she went tiptoeing to her shelves and climbed a little wooden ladder and started pulling the white boxes down and looking inside the tissue paper then at last she came back.

"Perhaps these sandals might serve your purpose, madam. They are every reasonably priced. They are in the sale as they are so small there is not much demand for this size." I tried the sandals, they were white and had peep-toes and guess what? They fitted me because I only had little feet – and I thought that they looked lovely. Even though they weren't satin slippers I was very pleased with them and even more pleased when Mam bought them. Then we set off home with Mam carrying the box in her carrier bag.

I sat on our bus and wondered what everybody at home would think when I put my shoes on. What would my sisters think? What would Grandma next door say? Maybe nobody would even recognise me, I would look so beautiful with them on – changed into a beauty in a flash. But when we walked down our lane nobody asked about my shoes and nobody was interested because they were all crowding round a van in our yard.

It was our new van. Uncle Sid and my dad took it in turns to sit in the driving seat – our dads were the only ones that could drive in our family. All the kids were crowded in the back which was supposed to be for a few animals or bags of animal food or bales of straw. Mam and me stood and stared at the new van – it was navy blue just like Mam's material for her costume for the wedding. Grandma stood with her arms folded and Aunty Vera, who was Uncle Sid's wife and Terry's mam, laughed and clapped at our new arrival. My mam said, "Well at least it's a serviceable colour."

Now we had a car and a van and it was decided that Uncle Sid and his family could have the car one weekend and Dad could have the van, then the next weekend they would swap. At first, we all thought that we would want our new van but we soon changed our minds because after a few sheep and pigs had been in the back it got quite smelly. There was always straw in there and sometimes a bag or two of corn and us kids had to sit on that and not on seats like in our car. We lost interest in our new van and anyway I had a lot of other things to think about. There was still my new tramp friend who slept in our bales every night. And there was the business of being beautiful to think of as well.

Ireney soon came again and I had to stand on our table while she saw what I looked like with my dress on. Mam hadn't done the hem yet but the rest was finished.

"Oh," said Ireney, "you are going to look lovely." Mam, with a mouth full of pins, started to work on getting my hem the right length. Then Ireney fished in her bag and brought out a decoration for my hair.

"It's a tiara," she said.

It was bright and sparkling and I just couldn't wait to get it on my head. I would surely change from lovely to beautiful in a flash when that was in my hair. But when Ireney tried to fix it on, it just flopped over my eyes and wouldn't stand upright. Then Mam got some hairgrips and tried to fix it but it was no use it just flopped every time they tried.

"It's her hair, it's so fine," said Mam. "Why don't I make her a little bonnet, Ireney? She could wear that instead and most of her thin hair would be covered."

Ireney agreed and I must say I was very disappointed at this setback to my plans to be beautiful.

"I won't look beautiful, I can't wear Ireney's tiara," I wailed as Dad came in for a mug of tea, but he just had no time for all this fussing about with shoes and dresses and the tiara.

"Beauty comes from within," he shouted as he rushed off to do his work on our farm which was our livelihood.

Ireney smiled her gummy smile and said that her big sister, who was also going to be a bridesmaid as well could wear the tiara and not to worry, it wouldn't be wasted. So that was the end of that, and my dress was pulled off and I stood there sadly in my navy knickers – which I now knew were serviceable. I also realised that navy was not my mam's favourite colour it was just that it didn't show the dirt. Ireney pushed the tiara back in her bag. I watched it disappear and I felt so sad. But Ireney smiled at me again, a real friendly gummy smile.

"You'll look lovely in a bonnet," she said, but a bonnet was not the same as a tiara. I ran to my tramp friend to cheer me up.

"Ah, ahh." He was sitting in our straw and was very pleased to see me and I took him some cheese and a mug of water again. And I told him about wanting to look beautiful for the wedding to make it my big day.

He drained the mug of every last drop of water and licked his fingers and smacked his lips. He lifted his dirty cap and scratched his sticky out hair.

"Beauty comes from within," he smiled his cracked skin smile.

"My dad says that."

"Well it's true. And in any case, you should not outshine the bride – it's her big day not yours after all." I sat down in the straw next to him and told him all about my dress and my new shoes till he fell asleep.

The Big Day came very quickly. After waiting for ages suddenly we had to hurry and get ready. I got washed in our wash house while Mam put her new costume on then she pulled my dress carefully over my head and she tied my bonnet in place and I put my sandals on. I ran upstairs and looked in the wardrobe mirror.

Well — I thought that I had done it at last. All the things together — my dress, my shoes and even my bonnet had changed me into a beauty in a flash. And if I didn't open my mouth when I smiled you couldn't see the gap in my teeth. Everything was as perfect as it could be.

One thing wasn't perfect though because at the last minute we realised that it wasn't Dad's turn to have the car. It was our turn to have our van and Uncle Sid and Aunty Vera had already gone out to Hull early this morning in the car. There was nothing for it but to go in our van. It was a good job that Mam's suit was a serviceable navy blue because she had to clean our van out even though she was all dressed up, while Dad put on his black suit and my sisters put on their best dresses. We all piled into our van, which was still a bit smelly, of course. What a squash it was. I had to sit on Mam's knee in the front and our Gwendy and Katy had to sit on bags of corn in the whiffy back.

We all piled out at Ringam church and there were two surprises for me. One was that Ireney had picked a posy of big red roses for me to carry and she had put a silver doyley round. And the other surprise was that her sister wasn't wearing the tiara, she was wearing a bonnet like me. She told me that Ireney knew how much I had liked the tiara and she thought that it would make me sad to see somebody else wearing it, so she took it back to the shop and got her money back. Then Ireney had made her sister a bonnet to match mine.

Everybody went into the church and we bridesmaids had to stand by the lychgate near the top of the church lane and wait for the bride. We waited and waited and stood there for ages and ages and I stared down the little lane and then at the hedge where a scrubby wild rose was growing quite near the lychgate.

With its tiny pale flowers, it wasn't a patch on my bunch of beautiful red roses. There was a crowd of villagers waiting to see the bride but Ireney was nowhere in sight.

Then all of a sudden, an old man in a creased suit came puffing up the lane and past the wild rose to Ireney's sister and me standing at the lychgate. He was Ireney's dad and he told us that the bride's old wedding car they had borrowed wouldn't start, he stood doubled up getting his breath back before racing into the church. Next thing we knew was that my dad was rushing out of the church to get the bride in our van. Nobody had a car to bring Ireney to church.

If Ireney was disappointed at coming in a smelly old van to get married, you could not tell. She got out and she beamed her gummy buck-toothed smile and she looked as if she could not have been more pleased if she had been getting out of Helen's dad's posh smooth car instead of our whiffy van.

Ireney seemed to glow as she walked up the aisle towards her groom. Her white silk dress was lovely of course and her veil and train made her look very important but it was her face that was beautiful. She looked more beautiful than anybody there – even more beautiful than me.

Everybody kept saying how lovely I looked but I knew that I didn't look beautiful like 'The Bride' – nobody did, she just looked better than us all with a beauty bursting out of her happiness inside her.

Then, when we came out of the church we all had to stand for photographs. I looked down the little lane and then back to the wild rose in the hedge near the lychgate and suddenly there was my tramp. I could hardly believe it – he was standing on the other side of the hedge peeping over and smiling at me. Then he waved his grubby hand and beckoned me over to him. Soon, they had finished taking photos of me and just wanted the bride and the groom. I made sure that no one was looking at me (well they wouldn't be – all eyes were on the bride of course because she looked so beautiful) then I crept to the lychgate. He was still beckoning and I slipped off to join my friend behind the wild rose bush.

'Ah, ah,' he was fumbling in his holey trousers.

"I want to show you something," he whispered and then he pulled his hand out and I could see what he was holding.

It was a penknife like Dad used to cut skin off dead lambs, only it was bigger than Dad's. And as he flicked the blade out I could see steel, hard and shining.

"Come here," he whispered but this time more urgently and he grabbed my hand. My little clean hand was in his dirty big hand. He had never touched me before. My lovely cotton bridesmaid dress with frills on its bodice was crushed against his dirty trousers and my white peep-toed sandals, which were not serviceable, were leaking squashy mud.

I stared frozen to the ground while my tramp slashed fiercely with his knife into the wild rose bush till there was hardly anything left of it except a knobbly root with a few brown shoots sticking up. Then he grabbed my posy.

"There," he said, "that should do, my beauty." And he carefully chose three roses.

Then he did another funny thing, he neatly cut the flowers off and jammed the bare stalks into the slashed old wild rose stems.

"Now that's called a graft and you will see it's true that beauty comes from within." He smiled his leather cracked smile and put a rose head in his button hole.

Then he walked off towards Hull. I heard his breathing one last time 'Ah aah'. I wiped my sandals on some grass and ran back to Ireney and the wedding party. And that was the end of that.

After the wedding, we all went to Ringam village hall for some tea and Ireney cuddled me and gave me a little present for being her good little bridesmaid. I opened the box and there was a little silver charm of a rose. I loved it and couldn't wait to put it on my bracelet. And that was the first thing I did when I got home.

I never saw my tramp again; he had moved on but I found out that it was not quite the end of that after all. You see, he had not been killed like my pet lamb. Dad said he would have gone to find more meat for work. And in any case, he had not quite gone from me because he had left me a lovely surprise. One day about a year later when I went to Ringam church something caught my eye just next to the lychgate. There were big red roses growing from right inside that ugly old wild rose root. It took your breath away they were so beautiful just like the roses from my bridesmaid posy.

I didn't put – good at being beautiful – on my list because I was not as beautiful as Ireney, instead I just put – being a good bridesmaid. It had been Ireney who shone with the most beauty because of happiness inside her.

Chapter 7

One Autumn Morning

Summer was over and it was sad to see that the petals had fallen from the roses at Ringam church. But something even more sad had happened. Well, it started to happen much earlier because I knew about it before I was a bridesmaid but I didn't want to say anything or even think about it. I was frightened because, you see, a Hull doctor said that I had to go into hospital and that meant to stay in. I had to go and have an operation and I was very scared.

Of course, I had been going for check-ups to the hospital ever since I could remember. My mam and me used to go on a bus to Hull and walk across the rubble of bombed out houses from the war. Mam said that going across the rubble was a short cut but I would rather have gone the long way round so that I didn't have to see the scattered broken bricks lying there like dead people. Some bricks still had pale distemper paint stuck to them and some had faded wallpaper on, with loose bits that flapped in the wind like torn material from the dresses of the dead little girls who used to live there. But there was no time to go the long way round, Mam said. She had to hurry and get back to help Dad with work on our farm, which after all was our livelihood, so we rushed on.

Then, when we got to hospital the rush seemed silly because we always had to wait for ages in the big crowded waiting room. We weren't paying to see this doctor like Dad had done when I was very little, this was the new free National Health so it was all different and not so quick and comfy.

A busy nurse called somebody's name but it wasn't mine. Nobody answered straight away because they had all been sitting there for so long that they had forgotten what they had come for. At first, Mam had been looking at some women's magazines, she liked doing that because she never had any time to sit and read at home. Come to think of it she never could have afforded the money to buy any magazines in the first place. Nearly all our money went back into our farm. I roamed about looking at pictures of innards from your cut open body. There were grinning skeletons, faces sliced in half and lungs with tubes going in. Eventually Mam got fed up of reading and I got fed up of looking at innards. Now we just sat on our wooden chairs as if we were stuck, gazing at the pale green distempered walls. I was bored but I didn't feel frightened because I knew what would happen, it was always the same.

When, finally, my name was called we didn't answer straight away, just like the last person. It took two or three shouts from the nurse before we realised our wait was over. In fact, we nearly missed our turn just like the last person. But finally, we got up, stiff from sitting so long, and walked into the examination room where I took my clothes off (all except my knickers of course) and the doctor asked me to breathe in and breathe out and cough. He looked at my skinny little body in my navy knickers and frowned. He listened to my chest with his stethoscope and frowned some more. Then he said again, "Breathe in... and... out." It was always the same and then I got dressed and then we went back to our house on the bus and Mam went out on our farm to help my dad. But then that one time it was different.

"I think we should have her in hospital, Mummy," said the doctor taking me by surprise. "We can do some cleaning up and taking out. I'm sure you'd be pleased about that, my dear." Now doctors might be pleased about cutting open people's bodies and cleaning them up and taking bits out, but I can tell you I was not so keen. I thought I was alright as I was. It was no good though, nobody was asking me, it was all arranged and my name went on the waiting list.

"I can't promise, of course, but I am hoping we can call her before too long," smiled the doctor as he closed my folder. "I hope the surgeon will see you soon." I got dressed as fast as I could. I didn't want to see any hospital doctor again soon and I couldn't wait to get out of there. I bet that Mam couldn't wait to get out of there either, she had to get back to work and she was late already. We rushed past all those others in the waiting room, fed up mams and bored kids, and we tumbled out onto the street. We had to pick our way through the dead bricks again and I didn't think that it was a good time for me to be thinking about dead things and so we headed for Gum as fast as we could.

After that everything seemed normal again and nobody mentioned operations at our house and there was the wedding to think of and I had such a good time. But then it was autumn and suddenly a big fat nurse came to see me (Mam said I had to say 'plump' as it was rude to say fat). Anyway, this nurse bustled in and put out some awful looking metal tools on our table. It was enough to make you feel poorly if you weren't already but I felt something else as well. I felt a sudden scald of fear shooting through me, I had never had it before and the burn was sharp and strong. I couldn't help myself I just ran off as fast as I could to try and get away. I ran to our woods and hid behind some old sand bags that had been put there in the war. This was where the foxes had their lair, they had dug through the rotting bags and through the sand to find a safe place. Of course, it wasn't long before I heard Mam shouting for me from our stack yard and I heard my sisters calling, but I stayed very still and I didn't come out till I saw the nurse's car go back up our lane.

Nobody said anything to me when I went back and I tried not to think about it hoping it would all go away and nothing would happen. But then one day, not long after the nurse had called, Posty came and brought a long white envelope for us with a Hull postmark. It was a letter from the hospital and that fear shot through my body again just like a bullet.

"It's an appointment for your operation," said Mam. "And the nurse will be coming again because she has to do some tests. I don't want you being silly and running away this time." Mam scowled at me. "I haven't got time to be rushing about looking for you." I ran upstairs and got into bed and hid under my quilt for safety. I took my lucky charm bracelet out from my mattress crack and put it on.

"You'll just have to be brave," said Mam the next morning and she was still scowling at me. She was in the middle of helping Dad with milking our cows and had dashed in to cook breakfast for us kids. The fat in the frying pan was too hot and it spat out angrily as Mam dropped our eggs in.

I knew what she said was true. And I also knew that I had been brave once and that was when I first went to school and I had stopped Charley Fox pushing Helen. In fact, I was surprised that I had not put – being brave – on my 'What I am good at' list when all that happened. But I had thought nothing of it at the time and anyway Miss Kenny and Brenda had helped me so maybe it didn't count. This time I was on my own.

The fat nurse (I was going to call her fat because I didn't like her, whatever Mam said) came for the second time and she put her stuff out again on our table, and then she took her navy gabardine coat off and rolled her sleeves up. I stood there frozen to our stone floor thinking she was going to cut me up and take my innards out there and then.

"There's nothing to be frightened of, my dear," she said smiling. Well she might have nothing to be frightened of it wasn't her that was having the operation. I licked my lips while that bullet of fear shot through me again but I knew it was no good running away now; Mam had warned me – I had to give in, what else could I do?

"Now come along, my dear," said the nurse. Then she jabbed a needle into my arm, looked in my mouth and hit my knees with a rubber hammer. I sat on our old couch and just let her do what she had to do.

"Good, well that's all – now that was nothing to be frightened about, was it, dear?" She smiled, patted my head and put her shiny tools back in her bag and clipped it shut. Then she rolled her sleeves down and put her gabardine back on. And that was the end of that.

I went to school and everything seemed normal again and I hoped again that if I didn't think about that operation it would go away and nothing would happen (but somewhere at the back of my mind I knew that it could). Anyway, that term we had started singing. I really enjoyed it and I found out that if I sang very loudly it drowned out my fear. We were learning a song about the hunter, John Peel.

"D'ye ken John Peel with his coat so gay..." I was glad he hunted foxes and I hoped he got them because they killed our hens, just because I forgot to get anybody to lock them up that time when I went to Helen's. I took a great gulp of breath and sang even louder as the hounds ran faster and faster to kill the fox and I was glad.

My dad and Uncle Sid used to kill foxes as well. But they didn't use hounds like John Peel – they used guns. They used to hunt the foxes down and shoot them.

My dad's gun was in a little room we called under-stairs. The rooms we had downstairs in our house were: our big room, passage, pantry, wash house and under-stairs. Under-stairs was the best. I used to go there and shut myself in and play with all the stuff that was there. At first you could only see our coats and wellingtons near the door but then further along there were all sorts of exciting, forbidden things. And as you got deeper and deeper in, the ceiling started to slope and you had to bend your head. And of course, it was dark, very dark with the door shut – there was no light under-stairs and you had to grope about and feel for things. It was a bit frightening but you could get out any time you wanted.

Dad's gun was kept right at the end of under-stairs. I used to go there bent double and hold that gun and feel its two cold oily barrels and its smooth wooden handle. His cartridges were in a box on a shelf above my head and I rolled them in my hands and smelt gun powder. Then one day last spring my dad's gun was not there.

Dad and Uncle Sid had gone into our woods with their guns, I saw them go and Dad had a spade over his shoulder as well.

It's not a boy!

They were hunting for foxes in the old sand bags in our woods. The sand bags had been a safe place for soldiers to hide behind in the war but now not so safe for the foxes. Dad and Uncle Sid were determined to dig the foxes out.

When they came back, Dad had a sack over his shoulder – they had dug into the fox's lair and shot the mother and father fox and brought this sack back. Dad threw it under our milk stand and you could see things groping about in there. Dad said that it was full of young foxes and there were too many to waste cartridges on. When he had gone, our Gwendy and me carefully opened the neck of the bag that was tied with binder twine and looked inside. There we saw some fox cubs and they just looked like little ginger puppies. They were lovely.

Suddenly, I began to feel a bit sorry for foxes always being hunted. I knew that they killed our hens but, after all, they had to eat and they had to feed their baby cubs. Dad always said 'There's always two sides to every story,' and I could see what he meant then.

Our Gwendy felt sorry for those cubs as well and so secretly we decided to feed them and bring them up as our very own. We took them some milk in a pet lamb's bottle and pushed the teat into their tiny mouths and they suckled greedily, while their little front feet pawed the air.

But next day when we went back with some more milk, the young cubs had gone and Dad said that he had thrown them in our drain with a brick in their sack. I could hardly bear to think of them going down and down in the dark water trying to gasp for breath and they could have looked up at the pale sky above them and struggled uselessly to get out. And now they were dead at the bottom of our drain. They would drift into the Humber and into the North Sea and that was the end of our springtime fox cubs.

Now though, as I have said, it was autumn and the leaves were falling just like the rose petals had and I tried not to remember the foxes because it was not a good time for me to be thinking about dead things with my operation coming up.

And that operation was nearer than I thought because the next day Mam said I hadn't got to go to school, so while our Gwendy and Katy set off to get their bus at our lane end I played about. I was surprised because I didn't feel any more poorly than I usually did but I didn't ask why I was staying at home. Then I found out – it was my day to go into hospital and now I finally knew that it was all really going to happen.

Mam asked Dad to take us and he agreed because an operation was more serious than just a check-up. It was much nicer for Mam and me to go in our car than to go on the bus. But we still had to hurry because my dad had to get back to feed our animals and they both had to do the milking at night. At least this time we didn't have to walk through the bricks lying there like dead people. Our little car sped through the streets of Hull.

And in a flash, I was sitting on a hospital bed wearing a nighty that Mam had made especially for my operation. Mam was in her navy wedding costume and Dad was in his funeral suit. Then they left me.

"Ta-ra," shouted Dad as they walked quickly down the children's ward and out through the door.

"You shouldn't say that, you should say 'Goodbye'," corrected Mam and they rushed off back to our farm to get on with their work. I was left in bed and there was no comforting crack in my mattress and no lucky charm bracelet to wear – no jewellery was allowed in here. I lay on my back staring up at that pale green distempered ceiling, way high up. And I was still there staring at the ceiling the next morning and there was no getting away from it.

"Hello, dear, I'm Nurse Gentle," said a nurse and she put me in a hospital nighty with a slit right down the back.

Then she was on to next girl. "Hello dear..." When she had finished going down the long line of kids in beds, she cleared her throat and talked to us in a loud voice.

"Now, children, you are all going to the theatre, isn't that nice?" I thought of Helen and her theatre and how good she was at dancing – yes it would be nice to go to a theatre again but of course you do not go to a theatre like Helen's, in a nighty with a slit up the back. Then Nurse Gentle was talking again so I had no time to think it all through.

"Now you are all going to meet Uncle Sid." Well of course I knew that it wouldn't be my real Uncle Sid he was at home ploughing in the fields on our farm – he looked after our fields while my dad looked after the animals. Then suddenly some doors swung open and out popped a man in a big green gown with a green hat on and white cloth round his mouth.

"Here he is children and you will all go to him in turn, isn't that nice?" smiled Nurse Gentle and she clapped and he took a bow like they did in Helen's theatre. Soon it was my turn and I went through the swing doors lying on a trolley. This of course, was not a real theatre.

This hospital theatre was a very little room and on each side of me there were two men with cloths over their mouths. All around the room there were shelves piled high with white sacks and boxes. It was a bit like the shop I had been to in Hull for my bridesmaid shoes except that these boxes were not full of shoes they were full of hospital stuff.

"Hello, I'm Uncle Sid," said one man in a jolly voice speaking through the cloth over his mouth so it went in and out as he spoke. "Now, there is nothing to be frightened of." And then he put a big mask over my face and there was a wheel inside and it started whirring and I tasted gas at the back of my throat. In a panic, I sat bolt upright gasping for air knocking the mask to the side.

"Now, now this won't do," said pretend Uncle Sid in a not so jolly a voice this time. And he and his helper both held me down and I could see that metal mask was ready to go over my mouth again and I knew that could be the end of me and I might die. I closed my eyes and let him do what he had to do.

The last thing I heard was pretend Uncle Sid singing in a big black deep voice, "D'ye ken John Peel..." and that wheel whirred and buzzed and I smelt that stench of gas and pretend Uncle Sid's voice got slower and slower and far away. And in my head, I saw the foxes running and running desperately trying to get away from the hunters.

"D'ye ken John Peel when he's far... far away..."

I didn't die, of course. I woke up in a line of trolleys with lots of other kids and I stared up at that green distempered ceiling again and waited. After a long time, my trolley was moved and Nurse Gentle came and wiped my face with a cold flannel. "There, that was nothing to be frightened of, was it? You'll soon be home, isn't that nice?"

Then ice cream was being given out – I had never had ice cream before and I couldn't wait. I sat up in bed. But when Nurse Gentle got to me she looked at my notes.

"Oh, you haven't had your tonsils out, you've only had your tubes cleaned – no ice cream for you I'm afraid – it will be your turn next time." And on she went with her bowls and spoon. 'Next time,' I thought. 'What is she talking about?'

I found out a few weeks later when I was at home because I saw Posty bring another long white envelope.

It was then that I went under-stairs again and shut the door so that I was in the dark. I went right to the bottom end and felt for Dad's gun – it smelt of death. And I wasn't playing anymore and I clicked the trigger. A bullet of fear scalded through me again and I felt the burn of the shot through to my innards.

I hadn't been shot, of course, because there were no cartridges in my dad's gun (they were on the shelf above my head like they always were) and I walked out of under-stairs quite safely. I knew that there was no such easy escape from going into hospital for the second time.

Mam and Dad left me there in a hurry again so that they could get on with our livelihood and I sat on that bed and looked up at that same high distempered ceiling and tears rolled down my cheeks.

It's not a boy!

"Halloo, what you doing here?" I turned and saw Charley – it was Charley Fox, from our school, on a trolley being wheeled from the theatre; he had had his tonsils out.

"Charley," I shouted. But his trolley was rushed off to the end row of our beds.

"He knows you, now isn't that nice?" said Nurse Gentle.

I had my second operation the next day and this time I knew I wasn't going to a theatre like Helen's. And I knew about the mask and the stench of gas and there was nothing I could do to stop it all happening again. I closed my eyes. I would surely die this time.

"Peel's 'view halloo' would awaken the dead..." I heard pretend Uncle Sid's big black voice fading away into deep water and this time I didn't see the foxes running from the guns in my head – no – I saw those baby fox cubs sinking with me in their sack. I looked up and saw that pale sky high up above the water. I clawed for air but couldn't get any because that stone was dragging us down to a death at the bottom of our dark drain. I was floating out to the River Humber and then into the North Sea, as dead as the foxes and the little girls from the bombed houses.

"Halloo." I came round from my gassy sleep to a loud noise.

"Halloo." It was Charley's grandma, she had come to take him home. Nurse Gentle told me that Charley's mam had died when he was a baby and his grandma had to look after him as best she could.

I must have had my tonsils out, at last, because my throat was really sore and I got my ice cream from Nurse Gentle. Wasn't that nice? Well it might have been but I couldn't eat all mine because I could hardly swallow. Anyway, it was all over and I supposed I must have been brave – I was certainly putting it on my 'What I am good at' list this time. After all I had been through I thought that I deserved it and I hadn't had anything on my list for ages.

"Halloo," shouted Charlie when I went back to school after a week or two. His clothes were raggy and dirty and he wiped his nose on his sleeve but I felt a bit sorry for him now I knew his mam had died. If only he hadn't tried to hurt Helen when she couldn't stick up for herself I could have liked him more.

"Why did you cry in hospital?" he suddenly shouted with a sly grin on his face. Everybody could hear so I had to think, quickly. I didn't want them thinking that I wasn't brave after all.

"I was crying for what you did to Helen," I lied. "Why did you hit her?"

"She said I was a 'dirty boy', so she deserved it." Well, that was a surprise to me I can tell you and it made me think even more about my dad's saying that there's always two sides to every story and now I couldn't put all the blame on Charley. And when we had singing again at school I didn't sing that song about hunting foxes as loudly as before because as you know I felt a bit sorry for the foxes as well as for Charley. Anyway, we were soon into winter and on to another song and that was the end of John Peel and frightening things like operations.

It's not a boy!

Chapter 8

Holidays

When winter was over at last we all looked forward to our summer holidays and I looked forward to finding something else to put on my 'What I am good at' list. I hadn't found anything at school yet so I thought that I might find something for my list in our holidays.

But when I say holidays I mean our long school holiday, at home, because our family didn't go away; we always stayed at home in Gum. You see, we couldn't easily go away for a long time because my mam and dad and Uncle Sid and Aunty Vera were always busy on our farm. They hadn't got time for a holiday. Our farm was our livelihood. And anyway, my dad said that there was no point in going away on holiday where anything could happen – it was better to stick to what you knew at Gum where you would be safe. But my mam didn't always agree with him because I once heard her say that she would like to go on holiday for a change. But we never did.

When us kids weren't helping out on our farm (which we often had to do) we just played about in our fields or woods doing the things we always had done. Sometimes though, I went to Brenda's at Sunkstead, which was the village just next door to Gum, and we rode down her lane with her sister Jeany in Lucky Basket's little cart like they always did. And sometimes Brenda came to stay with us at Gum and we ran about all day long shouting and laughing. Except on Sundays of course, because early on Sunday morning I always came home from Brenda's or Brenda went back to her own farm at Sunkstead. Sundays were not for Brenda or even for Gum.

You see, Sunday was a very different day of the week and I suppose Mam liked Sundays because it was a bit of a change and maybe it was a bit like a holiday for her. The first difference was that in the morning we all had to help on our farm because some of the farm workers had the day off, then in the afternoon Gwendy and me got ready to go to Elm Tree Cottage at Ringam.

First of all, our Gwendy and me bathed in the bathroom upstairs. You did not use our steamy wash house on Sundays – our wash house was too grubby for Sundays. We changed our knickers and pulled on our Sunday best dresses and we did this very quickly because it was always so very cold in our bathroom. Then we ran up our lane and jumped on the bus to Ringam. We walked down Green Lane and just before you came to Sunnyside where the Great Aunties lived, we came to Elm Tree Cottage where I had been born.

At Elm Tree Cottage, we played with our cousins Mary and Suzy who lived there. But when I said played I didn't mean play like we did at Gum, running in our fields and woods and making a noise – no, this was quiet sitting down play that you had to do on Sundays. We played little games like I Spy – and we read books. And sometimes we just sat near the fire with bright coals burning up and watched the flames with Aunty Martha telling us stories about angels. She said that Guardian Angels looked after us all and loved you whatever you did. And I often looked into the flames at Elm Tree Cottage and I thought could see an angel in a red dress leaping up and dancing. And if I was cold the angel with its face shining and glistening, leaped up even more and came out of the fire to wrap its warm wings round me and keep me warm.

And then sometimes, because there was all the time in the world at Elm Tree, we went out for a quiet stroll in the garden with gentle Uncle George and Aunty Martha. And even though it was only a little garden they had a great big elm tree in the middle. It was a beautiful weeping elm and I could tell that it was grafted because half way up the trunk you could see a rough mark were the beautiful part took over – just like on the tramp's rose. Anyway, we used to sit on a seat under that elm tree and you could see it hanging round and down almost to the ground – shining in the sun or glistening in the rain. And its leafy branches wrapped round you and kept you safe. It was like another Guardian Angel with wings to protect you. Even in the winter the branches wove together so closely that they made a little wooden umbrella like the angel's bones. We sat there under the elm till it was time for Sunday school.

Then we set off and quietly strolled, because you did not run on Sundays, down Green Lane and along to our chapel at Ringam. We sang gentle children's hymns and said our prayers. Then our Sunday school teachers told us Bible stories. Aunty Martha was one Sunday school teacher and I was in her group with Suzy. Ireney came as the other Sunday school teacher after she got married. Her big church didn't have a Sunday school so she came to our little chapel to teach the kids. Our Gwendy and Mary were in Ireney's group and so was Lenny Fox. Lenny was quiet, not at all like his brother Charley. Naughty Charley was in my group.

Charley used to go under the pews and scribble in the hymn books which you were not allowed to do. Aunty Martha could never turn her back on him for one minute because of what he might get up to. But she was never angry with him because you didn't have to be good for Aunty Martha to like you, she was kind to you whatever you did just like the Guardian Angels.

And so, of course, on our Prize Giving day, Charley got a book like we all did. We were given a book as a prize for coming to Sunday school. Everybody got one even if you had only been for a few times and even if you didn't behave when you came like Charley Fox. One year I had a book called *The Three Little Dogs*. And I sat down straight away near the fire at Elm Tree Cottage to read the story. It was about three dogs looking out of a pet shop window. They were all hoping and waiting to be sold and to go to homes of their own. And as I read I could feel a Guardian Angel flaming up to wrap round me and I needed it then because my story was not turning out too well. Two dogs got chosen at once and went to safe and loving homes but the last little Scottie dog did not get chosen and was left behind in the shop window to look out with big sad eyes. Everybody was rushing past and he was alone in the world. But I didn't read any more just then because it was tea time.

Very quietly and gently we took our chairs to the table and sat down. Then Uncle George said a prayer and we all whispered 'Amen' and then we had our tea.

We had potted meat 'sammies' (we never remembered to say 'sandwiches' like Mam told us to, even on Sundays); they were made with pure white bread and the crust was cut off. We always had to eat our crusts at Gum because Mam said that crusts made you hair curl. Mind you, it hadn't worked for her yet because her hair was dead straight and she had to have perms. Anyway, the next thing we ate was a shop bought sponge cake with white icing and pale little sugar flowers on the top. Then there were jellies in waxed paper dishes with concertina sides. It was all like angel food.

After tea, Mam and Dad came to Ringam with Katy in our van or car depending on whose turn it was. We all went to chapel and Uncle George preached to us and when it was over he said 'Amen' again very gently and then we all whispered 'Amen' and then we went home. That was the end of our angel holiday till next week. Mam's 'bit of a change' had come to an end and I expect she looked forward to next Sunday.

But in the long summer holidays she had a bigger change than ever. You see, Aunty Martha organised our Sunday school trip. I saved up my pocket money for our outing but it was not much and there was no other money. As you know, I had to help out on our farm when needed especially on Sundays – everybody did – but us kids didn't get any money for doing it because it was our livelihood. So, it took me a long time to save a little bit of money for our trip.

One year we were going to Scarborough and it was the furthest we had ever been. We would be going out of East Yorkshire for a whole day which was very different for us. It would be even more of a change than Sundays at Elm Tree

Cottage. And because we were going away anything could happen, like Dad said.

On the day of this trip Mam was up earlier than usual because she had to help with the milking and then make us some sammies for our packed lunch. First, she cut slices of brown bread with thick crusts and filled them with mashed boiled eggs – we always had eggs because they didn't cost anything. There were loads of eggs from our hens now that I remembered to lock them up at night to keep them safe from the fox. Then Mam cooked Dad's breakfast – he always had eggs, with bacon from our own slaughtered pigs. And while Mam was rushing about we were getting dressed into our sundresses.

At the last minute, I remembered my bucket and spade and I searched frantically under-stairs and went deeper and deeper with my back bent. They were on the floor near Dad's gun and I grabbed them quickly and ran outside to where Dad was waiting in our van impatiently revving the engine. He was in a hurry because he wanted to get on with his work and today he wouldn't have Mam to help so there would be more than ever to do. But then at another last-minute Mam thought that it looked like rain and she jumped out to get our macs. Then we were really ready and our van rushed off bumping along our country road and into the Main Street at Ringam. We could see our yellow holiday bus waiting. It was not a serviceable navy blue like our usual East Yorkshire buses – no, the holiday bus was a little country bus and was bright yellow all over.

I clambered up the steep bus steps and there was Suzy already in a seat waiting for me – Uncle George had given her half a crown to spend, so she was very pleased. We settled down on fuzzy yellow seats with black shells woven on them to remind us of the seaside. We were so excited but as we stared through the windows we saw heavy grey skies.

"Look out for enough blue sky to make a pair of sailor's trousers," shouted Mary hopefully. "Then it will be a fine day." We all looked out and I could just see a little strip of blue but I thought that even my mam, who was very clever with materials, could not make a pair of trousers from that. Even if it was a very thin sailor she couldn't do it with such a tiny blue remnant. But I kept on staring out and hoping that my little patch of blue would grow while our bus filled with all the families crowding into their seats.

Dads didn't come on our trip – they were all busy working – but mams and grandmas came. Except my grandma didn't come because she thought, like Dad, that Gum was the safest place to be. Ireney didn't come either as she wanted to cook for her husband. But all the Sunday school kids came of course – even naughty Charley, with his big loping quiet brother Lenny and two more of his older brothers. Their grandma came and she heaved up the steps – and then to everybody's surprise Charley's Dad got on. He was wearing a shiny black suit and his jet-black hair was oiled down. It was most unusual for dads to come because as I've said they were at work – but not Charley's dad who was always very quiet and usually sat about doing nothing. My mam must have been thinking the same as me because I saw her staring at him, but then he winked at her and she quickly looked away.

Suddenly our bus engine took a heaving throbbing breath.

"Everybody here?" shouted the driver throwing his cigarette butt out of the window and then he pushed the great gear stick and we juddered off grunting and groaning down the Main Street.

We waved goodbye to Ringam's empty houses and then after that Suzy and me settled down in our seats. We opened our purses and looked at our money, me with a few coins and Suzy with her shiny half a crown. Then we took our macs off and tried throwing them up onto luggage rack but they were bulging with everybody else's macs and baskets full of sammies. So, we gave up and played.

At first we played 'I Spy' and some other quiet Sunday games until Charley, who was with all the other naughty boys on the back seat, started to sing and we all joined in. One of the songs we sang was 'How much is that doggy in the window?' and it reminded me of my *Three Little Dogs* book that I hadn't finished reading yet. We sang songs at the top of our voices till we couldn't sing anymore and then we just sat quietly again listening to our bus grunting and groaning on its way to Scarborough. I looked out of the window and saw that the heavy grey clouds were rolling away and great patches of blue were being woven in the sky. Now there was easily enough blue material to make a pair of trousers even for a fat (sorry, Mam; I should have said plump) sailor and we might not need our macs after all.

Ages and ages later we tumbled out into the bus park in Scarborough. Then we all trudged off down a lane carrying heavy baskets of food, and towels and swimming things and of course our macs – just in case it rained. We walked for ages down and down then suddenly we were there and the sand and sea were waiting for us. And now the sun shone down warmly and we settled ourselves in a space on the sands. Mam got some deckchairs and we put our swimming cozzies on. None of us could swim but when we were at the seaside we always wore our shirring elastic bumpy swimming costumes that our mams had made us.

Suzy and me dug in the sand and made huge holes that we filled with sea water and we ran backwards and forwards to the far away waves with our buckets. We dug huge mounds of sand which we patted smooth and decorated with shells that we had collected from the beach. Then after we had eaten our packed lunch Suzy and me went off to buy an ice cream.

We went to a van on the sands, Charley's Dad was there at the van waiting to buy an ice cream as well, at least I thought that's what he was doing but he stayed there so long talking to the girl behind the counter that I think he must have forgotten what he came for. Anyway, he let us go first and we both bought a cornet and of course it tasted even better than the ice cream I had in hospital after my operation, which I couldn't eat much of anyway because of my sore throat.

Then Suzy and me put our sundresses back on and went off to spend the rest of our money. We had a great time looking in shops on the promenade and in a sweet shop there was a paper plate set out with bacon and eggs just like Dad's breakfast only in seaside rock, if you see what I mean. And there were hundreds of things for us to buy and you just couldn't decide what to choose. In the end, Suzy bought a red hair slide and a little ring with a red stone that matched her red dress. I didn't like red anymore, because of my pet lamb paying for my red coat with his life, but I didn't tell Suzy and I couldn't decide what to buy.

"Two fat ladies 88," shouted the Bingo man from his little round stall with a tent roof where families sat staring at their number tray. My mam would not like him saying 'fat' and anyway she said Bingo was not the thing for people who wanted to get on in the world so we never played.

"Try your luck," shouted the man and he winked at me and he pushed a number tray on a string towards us but we ran off and nearly tripped over each other to get away laughing together. It was very crowded and Suzy was ready to go back now she had finished her shopping, I watched her join our families on the sand. Then I went back along the prom and concentrated for a long time looking for something special. Suddenly there it was, just what I wanted. It was a little yellow plastic Scottie dog with a loop that would go onto my charm bracelet. It reminded me of my story and that last little dog sitting looking out at the world with no home to go to. Of course, I bought it and then dashed to get the egg and bacon rock on a plate as a present for Dad and then I had spent up.

Now I was ready to go back to our group on the sands. But suddenly even more people seemed to have crowded in and I couldn't see anybody I knew anywhere. I saw so many heads, so many striped deckchairs and so many kids rushing about with buckets and spades. I searched up and down frantically but I had completely lost my way now and couldn't even see the rock shop I was in a minute ago. Hot sun was beating down on me because that blue patch in the sky had grown even more and would fit an enormous sailor now.

"Unlucky for some — number 13," shouted another Bingo man, and suddenly I saw old Mrs Fox sitting with her Bingo tray and there was Charley and Lenny and the brothers. Mr Fox was nowhere in sight maybe he was still waiting to buy his ice cream. I shouted frantically as the crowds surged. "Hey, Charley!" And he looked up from his tray of numbers and saw me and laughed but I was pushed on by the crowd and the Fox family disappeared. I was alone in the world with everybody rushing past me.

I raced on and I was going away from the prom and towards a sort of park — and I was in a panic. I kept thinking that our little yellow bus might go back home without me and leave me behind and I would have to stay in Scarborough in the dark night on my own. And then anything could happen. I could hardly breathe with worry and took great gulping sobbing breaths. But by the time I reached the green trees at the end of the prom the crowd was thinning out and I could catch my breath and calm down. I decided to look around again for somebody I knew.

Suddenly there was Mr Fox coming towards me. His shiny suit glistened in the sun and his oiled hair shone like a halo, his face was all smiles. Maybe he was changing into a Guardian Angel for me. But, no, he was not — because he was not on his own and he was not even smiling at me — he was walking arm in arm with the ice cream girl. They were staring into each other's eyes. I waved and shouted but they only had eyes for each other and they crossed over the road and walked away and disappeared up the leafy woodland, stopping every now and again to kiss.

Now, I was really on my own and had to decide what to do. I looked around carefully and although I didn't see anybody, a plan came into my head in a flash. I went up to a tree in the park and sat down in the shade on the grass with the knobbly trunk at my back. I clutched my two paper bags with my rock breakfast and my plastic yellow Scottie dog. And I watched and waited and waited.

Then after a long, long time I saw them coming like I hoped they would. I saw them weaving through the noisy crowds and heat. I saw a bright red dress fluttering and flying down the prom like gentle flames making their way towards me. It was Suzy, running and pointing with her mam following. She was so close now I could see her sparkling hair slide and glass gemstone ring flashing on her finger.

"I knew you'd be here," she shouted wrapping her warm arms round me. And we all looked up to the grafted trunk and then up and up into the leafy wing branches. It was a weeping elm tree of course.

Mam was waiting anxiously on the sands and I was sure that she was pleased that I was safe but she gave me a look like the one she gave Mr Fox but I didn't think that I ought to wink at her like he had done.

Then it was time to go home and we packed our things up, shaking sand from everything and struggled back up the hill to the bus park. There stood our yellow bus patiently waiting and we all got on and settled back into our seats ready to go home.

Except that we could not go home yet because Charley's family hadn't come back to the bus. We waited and waited and still they did not come. The bus driver got out and walked round smoking another cigarette. Then he paced up and down impatiently. The sun was getting low in the sky. It was cold and we put our macs on – glad of them after all. And we kept on staring out of the window and down the streets hoping that the Fox family would turn up.

Then all of a sudden, there they were strolling across the car park eating fish and chips from greasy newspaper wrappings. Loping Lenny was hugging a big teddy bear that he had won on Bingo and Charley was pulling a mongrel dog on a piece of string. He said that he had found it wandering the streets and claimed it for his own – he kept tossing it a chip and the dog tried to catch it as it was dragged along. But we were not on our way home yet because Mr Fox was not with his family.

"Oh, leave him," laughed Grandma Fox as she settled in her seat on the bus. "He has other fish to fry tonight – he gets up to all sorts of things when your back is turned." And so, at last, the bus driver pushed the gear stick and our bus set off from Scarborough to grunt and groan all the way home. I was pleased to be going back at last.

Going on trips was all very well but it was not always safe and Guardian Angels were hard to find when you needed them. Anything could happen when you went away.

And of course, I didn't get anything to put on my 'What I am good at' list because you didn't have to be good at anything for Sundays and trips. Guardian Angels and Aunty Martha liked you whatever you did, you could be good or bad, it didn't matter. And that was all very well, but as you know I really needed things to put on my list so I was not too happy about that.

One thing that did please me though was my little dog charm. And that night when I snuggled up on my straw mattress, I put my Scottie dog on my chain safely with the wren, the ballet dancer and the rose. Then I finished reading my story about the three dogs at last and of course the last dog did get what he had been hoping for. It turned out that a little boy, all raggy and poor, chose the dog and got him cheaply because nobody else had wanted him. And so that pleased me as well. Now everybody was safely home at last, except Mr Fox who had been left behind in Scarborough.

Mr Fox did not come home for a long time and when he did, he was married to the ice cream girl. And they all lived together in their little terraced house with Grandma Fox and the boys and the mongrel dog on a string.

Oh, and Dad quite liked his rock – at least he smiled a bit at it, but he didn't eat it because he said he'd rather eat eggs from our own hens and bacon from our own pigs at Gum like he

always did. He said that he would rather stick to what he knew
– just to be on the safe side.

Chapter 9

Still Waters

After our trip to the seaside Dad was very surprised that Mr Fox came back married to the ice cream lady and he said that still waters run deep because Mr Fox was usually very quiet and just sat about doing nothing but suddenly he did something that took you by surprise. Anyway, we soon had something else to think about because it was time for us kids to go back to school. Our long summer holiday was over and off we went to our lessons again.

Mam and Dad said that I was growing up but I wasn't so sure because I didn't seem to be learning very much at my school. I was not finding anything I was good at. You see, I wasn't in my first class for long and I hadn't got time to learn anything much before I had to go up into Miss Hart's class. I had to move up because there was no room for me in the Infant class anymore because there were so many new kids starting school.

I didn't mind moving up into Miss Hart's class though because she was so kind to me and not at all like my first teacher who was always so strict. That teacher had not liked me on my first day at school when I hit out at Charley Fox and it wasn't my fault as you know because he hit me first. Miss Hart would have taken my side straight away because she liked me.

As well as liking me, Miss Hart had decided that I was too delicate for lessons and said that I needn't do much work in class because I had been poorly as a baby and was not strong enough. She said that I could go outside and play to get some good fresh air in my lungs any time I wanted – and I wanted to quite a lot of times. So you can see how I didn't learn very much and didn't get to be good at anything in my new class either. I hardly did any lessons.

Then Miss Hart started bringing me an orange every week because she said I needed building up and oranges would make me strong. She didn't have any kids of her own because she wasn't married and everybody likes to have something or somebody to look after. So, she sort of claimed me as her own when I was at school, I suppose I was a bit like that mongrel dog on a string that Charley had claimed for his own at Scarborough. Anyway, whatever the reason, I loved the oranges she brought me – I had never had an orange before. At our house, all the fruit us kids ever had was from our orchard. We had our sour apples and hard pears and squashy plums half sucked up by hungry bees. You had to be careful if you picked the fruit with a bee sucking because they didn't like being bothered and they didn't want to give up their fruit and so they stung you. But if we dodged the bees we could go out and eat as many apples, pears or plums as we wanted and we quite liked them – we didn't know any different. But oranges – well, they tasted so much better than any fruit I had ever tasted. And do you know? I didn't agree now with Dad about sticking with what you were used to just to be on the safe side. And that was because Miss Hart's oranges were new to me and they didn't do me any harm. To be honest I liked them very much. And so, when everybody else was in class working hard at their lessons, I was often sucking at those big juicy orange lumps on my own in the playground.

Then one day when kind Miss Hart gave me my orange I put it in a pocket in my mac which was in our cloakroom and then went into our classroom. I thought that I would go out of class when I got a bit tired of lessons like I always did. I would put up my hand and tell Miss Hart that I needed some fresh air. But on that day Charley beat me to it. He must have been tired of the lesson as well because he put up his hand and asked to go to the lavvy (Mam said 'Say lavatory.') and he didn't come back for ages. We all knew that trick, you could get away for a long time like this and miss a lesson. Anyway, when Charley finally got back after being outside for ages it was my turn and I asked to go out. Of course, Miss Hart said, "Yes," and I went straight to my mac to get my special orange. I was looking forward to eating it – in fact I could hardly wait to sink my teeth into that orangey juicy flesh. But my orange wasn't there. I couldn't believe it. I searched both pockets again and again but they were flat and empty. My orange had gone.

Kind Miss Hart came over to help me search but it was no use, my orange was still not there. Then Miss Hart spotted something I had missed. There were huge chunks of peel all over the cloakroom floor. I don't know why I didn't notice them. I suppose I had been just concentrating on searching my pockets for my big juicy orange and not looking around for peel. Miss Hart called for Charley straight away.

"Charley, what do you know about this missing orange?"

"Nothing, Miss," said Charley.

"Open your mouth, Charley." And when he opened his mouth you could see bits of orange in between his teeth and his tongue was orange as well.

"Why did you take the orange?" Miss Hart asked patiently.

"I was hungry, Miss, I couldn't help it." And so Charley had to stand next to the dripping tap in our cloakroom again at playtime. And I didn't have my orange that day but I wasn't too worried because I knew Miss Hart would bring me another one.

My delicious weeks in kind Miss Hart's class floated easily into one another with oranges and fresh air. And in no time at all I was in the next class without getting anything more on my 'What I am good at' list. And Miss Hart had to let me off her bit of string and I could not be her special pet to look after any more. I was growing up a bit more and so I left Miss Hart for ever and went to The Huts.

You see, my next lessons were not in our main school building – our school was by now even more full of kids and there was no room for our class. So, Miss Kenny had to come to school early and take us to The Huts. Every day we had to trudge down there come rain or shine. In winter, all of us went in our wellies just in case it was raining which it often was. My dad bought me some new ones from our cobbler in Ringam and they were a size too big so I could grow into them. We walked through Ringam every day and passed the end of Green Lane on our way to The Huts – they had been used by the army in the war. They were old grey sheds with rusty metal windows and they stood in some forgotten overgrown rough land. One hut was derelict and then there was a row of outdoor lavs – like at our main school – and then there was our hut classroom with some boarded up windows and a smoky stove in the corner. All in all, you would think that it would be a horrible place to go to – but it wasn't.

The Huts was a lovely secret place where our class went and hid every day. Our new teacher was Mr Grey and he was very gentle, a bit like Miss Hart, except that he didn't bring me oranges. In fact, he didn't seem to notice me or any of us very much at all. And nobody from the main school even seemed to remember our class was there until Miss Kenny came to collect us at home time to go back through Ringam to catch our bus. We, more or less, seemed to be able to please ourselves all day long.

And gentle Mr Grey seemed to please himself as well. In the autumn and winter, he lit the smoky black stove and we all kicked our wellies off at the door so as not to paddle water onto the concrete floor. Then we sat round the stove in a semicircle staring at the bright coke through a little glass window while Mr Grey read us stories. We just sat there in our stocking feet with our stove giving out its red glow until Mr Grey's gentle voice gradually faded to a whisper and sometimes he went all dozy and sleepy. He sat there in his teacher's chair near the smoky stove while we got up quietly and went to our desks to paint pictures.

In spring and summer, though, Mr Grey actually started to teach us – he did lessons about bees all the time. You see, he loved bees and he kept a hive just outside our classroom window and because some more windows got broken and nobody remembered to board them up, his bees buzzed in and out of our classroom all day long. Gentle Mr Grey taught us not to be frightened of them and he even let them land on him and go into his black curly hair and they even sat on his nose. They crawled all over his holey jumper and on to his creased trousers and still he didn't move a muscle. But come to think of it, that was not unusual because he hardly ever moved a muscle anyway. He didn't seem interested in anything much except bees. And when he talked to us about them his face lit up. He told us that if you kept very still the bees wouldn't sting you. If you just let them crawl in your hair or sit on your nose, they wouldn't hurt you; it was only if you bothered them that they would go for you like when we pinched plums off them. And in the warm weather gentle Mr Grey would ask if we were hungry and we always said that we were because we knew what came next. He got us some honeycomb from the hive. Now, he knew this would bother the bees so he sent smoke all over them from a puffer and the bees went dozy and didn't behave normally and so they didn't sting you. Mr Grey could now take away some of their combs and they were dripping with honey. We all had a little bit and after we had gobbled up the runny honey we chewed the waxy comb for ages even when we were in class and Mr Grey did not mind. He didn't even notice because he would be telling us some more things about his bees.

He told us about the quiet male bees who seemed to just sit about doing nothing but when a queen bee flew by they suddenly did something that took you by surprise. These quiet males flew after her to mate her.

"Still waters run deep," said Dad.

Then Mr Grey told us about the worker bees that were busy all summer long collecting nectar and making honey for us to eat. Oh! I loved those lessons, they were so interesting. At last I was learning something at school and soon I was good at knowing everything about bees.

And I also soon knew everything there was to know about birds as well. You see, there was that rough old land round The

Huts. Brenda and me loved it and in the spring, we sneaked about into this bit of land with its rough tall grass and wild bushes and it was like our own secret hideout. We watched birds making nests and mating then laying eggs and feeding their babies. They were so interesting and that's how I was good at knowing everything about birds. And so, I had something more to add to my 'What I am good at' list again. I was good at birds and bees. And I was very happy except for one thing and that was because Charley started causing trouble again.

He had started lifting up girls' skirts at playtime. And then he shouted, "Seen your knickers." And that was a nuisance because he started to chase girls with his gang of rough lads and they ran shrieking into our secret hideout and trampled all over. It spoilt it for our birds and frightened them away. I wished that Charley was more like Mr Grey's bees that never bothered you if you didn't bother them.

But Charley wasn't like the bees and he carried on annoying the girls until one day he tried to lift Brenda's skirt and so I went with Brenda to tell Mr Grey. Just in a gentle way, you understand, we knew Mr Grey would not get angry. And he didn't, he just had a word with Charley.

"Now, Charley, I'm sure your big brother Lenny doesn't do anything like this, he is a quiet boy. Now run along and play properly." Mr Grey was always kind to us, however bad we had been just like the Guardian Angels at Elm Tree Cottage. He always forgave us and believed we would be good from then on. But I'm afraid to say that when Charley did 'run along' like Mr Grey said, he just ran along to the next girl and lifted her skirt. Anyway, at least he didn't bother Brenda and me again and we were left alone to have a good time and be happy at The Huts again.

And while I was having a good time at school us kids were also having a good time at home as well. You see, Terry, from next door, had spotted a courting couple coming down our lane just before it got dark. Terry always knew about exciting things and he took us down our lane to where we could watch what was happening.

They came most nights, walking down our lane holding hands and he looked such a nice, quiet, young man. He smiled gently and listened to his girlfriend as she chatted away to him. He helped her climb over our gates and one night they went all the way to our Bottom Field next to our drain. We followed at a distance creeping along, hiding behind trees and hedges.

Then when they got to our Bottom Field they went a little way down the drain bank and went into some long grasses near a bush. And that's when it all started. We were watching safely from behind another bush and we saw them cuddling. They thought that they were on their own and nobody could see them but there was always one or two of us watching. It was great fun. They did the same thing every night, first they put their arms round each other then they kissed and then they lay down and kept on doing that cuddling sometimes for hours on end. And we just couldn't stop watching them waiting to see what would happen next but then something did happen and it put an end to it all.

One night I went there on my own to watch our courting couple. I found a nice bit of dried grass near another bush halfway down the bank of our drain and I settled down to watch them. And I could hear them talking.

"I am so hungry, I just can't help it," I heard the young man say, and I wondered if they'd got some food there because that's just what Charley said when he ate my juicy orange. And it's what we told kind Mr Grey when we wanted some honey. So I leant a bit further and peered round the bush to see what they'd got and that's when it happened.

I suddenly started to slide down the drain bank, I grabbed out at a little branch on the bush I was hiding behind but it snapped off. Then I scrabbled at a tuft of dry grass but it tore out in my hand. The mud was wet and there was no foot hold at all. I was on a slippery slope and our drain was waiting for me – all it had to do was keep still and wait. Our drain was smooth and quiet on the surface but underneath its water would take you by surprise because it was very deep.

My new wellies reached the water first and I heard the splash and then I could feel them being sucked under as they filled with murky water. In a panic, I groped again for something – anything – but now there was only fresh air, that good, clean, fresh air that I had so easily breathed when I was in kind Miss Hart's class. It was no use to me now.

In I went sliding down with my body pressed on the wet mud. After my wellies filled with water my belly got sucked in and I gasped at the cold and all my innards jumped up into my chest in shock. But there was no escape because next, in went my chest. I was out of my depth.

Up and up went the water until I retched at the thick slimy stuff on my tongue and in my throat. And still it rose, it thundered into my ears roaring round and round. I closed my eyes and slid down into the dark, black water.

I went down and down and of course I couldn't swim and so I knew I must drown. Mud and weeds wrapped round me as I dropped and dropped helplessly. Branches and grasses that I had grabbed at in vain bent over and looked into the water and stared at my death. I was going to join those poor little ginger fox cubs and my bones would end up with theirs in the North Sea after all. It was their dark grave and it would be mine. I could do nothing and this was no dream like in hospital.

Then all at once I hit a rock and my feet felt a solid lump in that slimy, oozing watery world. And suddenly I knew what to do. I kicked against that rock and Miss Hart's oranges must have worked and made me strong because I kicked hard. I fought for all I was worth even harder than when I had fought Charley on my first day at school. I kicked and kicked and my water-heavy wellies finally floated off and then suddenly I was going up. I burst above the water and opened my eyes to the blurry light. My mouth opened and I gasped for that delicious fresh air. I was ready to shout 'Help' but I was too late. I was on my way down again. I stuck my arms out and reached up high but of course there was nothing there except fresh air.

And it was then that I felt somebody grab my hands and pull and I was heaved up through the blackness like a baby being born. I gasped and sprawled onto the grass and when at last my eyes cleared that nice young lad, who was hungry, was leaning over me while his girlfriend rubbed me down with her coat and then they ran off, back up our lane.

It was a long, long time before I could get up and go back home. I was very cold and shivering, I can tell you. And when I told Mam what had happened she was mad at me for losing my wellies because they were new and they cost hard-earned money. Anyway, I had to get washed in our wash house and then go to bed in case I caught my death of cold.

I didn't catch my death, but I did get a cold and I had to stay in bed and have a day off school. Then, when I went back to school, Brenda told me that Lenny had been in real trouble. You see, news of Charley's game of lifting girls' skirts at The Huts had travelled down to our main school. And the big lads there started doing it as well, thinking that it would be fun. And it caused the girls to go round our big playground screaming and there were a lot of mams coming to school to complain. Then the game stopped after a stern word from our Headmaster. But yesterday, Lenny who had so far kept out of this game, as he was a quiet lad and usually kept himself to himself, suddenly took everybody by surprise and jumped out and lifted a girl's skirt and that would have been alright because he would just have had another stern word from our Headmaster. But he didn't stop there he went and pulled the girl's knickers down.

"Seen your bottom," he shouted. It was as if he was one of Mr Grey's smoked bees and he had gone all dozy and wasn't behaving normally. But nobody was making any excuses for Lenny's behaviour, of course, and you can imagine what a fuss it all caused. Our Headmaster got his cane out. I had seen it before – it was a thin whippy stick like Dad took to Hull livestock market. Well, Brenda said that Lenny begged and wailed not to be caned and you could hear his screams all over our big school. He said that he was sorry and he would never do it again and he ran outside but he was dragged back and caned there and then.

But that was not the end of it. You see, after that Lenny disappeared – he was nowhere to be found. He didn't go home to his little house with the dog on a string that night. And he didn't come to school today either. Nobody knew where he was.

Except me – I found out where he was. You see, after school I wandered back to Bottom Field just to see if I could find my wellies, my dad had not bought any new ones yet. I had to wear my school shoes out at play and then clean them in the morning for school and that was boring. So I was keen to find my wellies even though I knew it was hopeless and that they would surely be out in the North Sea by now next to the little fox cub bones. Anyway, it was worth a try. I could see my mud skid marks down the bank but of course there was no sign of my wellies. There was a sign of something else though.

I heard a snuffling noise coming from the courting couples bush and I leant over very carefully so as not to fall into our drain again and there, in long grass, cold and shivering was Lenny. I didn't know what to do. If I told a grown up, he might be caned again for running away so I told Terry instead because he always knew what to do. Then I had another idea. I ran back home and made a sammy like I had done for my tramp and then I got a mug of water I ran down our lane carefully so as not to spill the water and I took it to Lenny.

"I've run away," said Lenny as he munched hungrily between sobs. "And I'm never going back; I'm going to hide for ever." And he wouldn't budge so I had to leave him there and it would soon be dark. And I was worried about him. But I needn't have worried because when I was supposed to be in bed, I was standing on our windowsill looking through our bedroom window and I saw the police. They were in our lane and heading down to our Bottom Field with big torches and tracker dogs. And striding out in front and leading the way was Terry.

108

Of course, Lenny was rescued and he was carried by a policeman safely home in a blanket. And next morning when I told my dad the story of quiet Lenny he said again, "The quiet ones are always the worst – still waters run deep."

Everything was alright at last. Lenny was forgiven for what he had done because he had been given his punishment by being out in the cold and everybody was so relieved that he was safe. And anyway, we soon had something else to think about. Because not long after all that we found out that the new Mrs Fox was expecting a baby.

Well, she already had four of Mr Fox's kids to make her own and look after so I didn't know why she needed another.

"I don't know how she is going to manage with another one in that little house with all those boys," said Mam. "Especially after that quiet one has been in trouble."

"Why is she having another one then?" I asked.

"She couldn't help it," said Mam. "You saw what the courting couple were up to – so you know all about the birds and the bees." Well of course I saw them and of course knew about the birds and bees from Mr Grey's class. And as you know, it was already on my 'What I am good at' list but I didn't see how that had got anything to do with Mr and Mrs Fox's new baby. Mam looked at me carefully and it was funny but somehow, I knew there was something I didn't know. I was out of my depth again like I had been when I was drowning in our drain. But this time there was no kind young man to grab my hand and rescue me.

Then suddenly my dad came in with a brown carrier bag and he rescued me, in a way, because he stopped Mam looking strangely at me. You see, he had bought me some more wellies from Ringam – they were a size bigger than my last ones. They were far too big. I didn't say anything but I knew now that I wasn't as grown up as Mam and Dad thought I was.

And I never could find out from our courting couple what they were really doing that was like my birds and bees. You see, they never came down our lane ever again.

It's not a boy!

Chapter 10

Glades

I didn't go near our drain for a long time after the time when I nearly drowned. I had learnt my lesson there. But at school I was soon to find that I had not learnt my lesson about some things that were very important and that there were consequences for this.

You see, after a year, our class had to go back to the main school. Gentle Mr Grey got a new class and we had to leave him and The Huts for ever. Our new teacher was now the Headmaster's wife and she was called Mrs Bantam.

Mrs Bantam was very bossy indeed and she decided that I needed to do much better with my school work. She was not at all interested that I had learnt about the birds and bees at our huts because the only important things now were sums and spelling. Even being poorly was no excuse to her. If I was away from school I still had to do her tests just the same as all the others when I got back. And if I got nought out of ten, which I usually did, I had to stay in when the others went out to play and I had to work in my own time. Mrs Bantam said that there were consequences to your behaviour, so if you got bad scores you had to pay and that was sad for me.

Even my 'What I am good at' list could not cheer me up because I was bad at sums and spellings and they were the lessons that counted in Mrs Bantam's class. Kind Miss Hart and Mr Grey always let me off but Mrs Bantam never did and now my life would never be same again. Oh, how I longed to be eating Miss Grey's oranges in the fresh air or to be with gentle Mr Grey at The Huts again. All I had in my head in those days were birds and bees. Now I had to have sums and spellings in my head or else there would be sad consequences for me. Everything was different at school now.

But at least when I went home everything was still the same there. And because I was not going to our drain I started going into our woods. I loved going there. It was full of tall trees and I gave them all names like my family. There was a big old oak and that was my dad so strong and proud he would not bend for anything. Mam's tree was a sycamore with its branches arranged very carefully – in step-by-step order with not a leaf out of place just as if they had been sewn on. Uncle Sid's was a beech tree standing up above all the other trees and seeing all there was to see. Aunty Vera's was a willow that danced in the wind and its leaves made a shadow pattern on the floor like her pretty dress. But even though I loved going in the woods there was something you had to know. If you went there you had to be careful. You see, there was a person we had to look out for when we were in the woods and he was not part of my family – he was called Mr Lordly and I was quite scared of him – well all us kids were.

Mr Lordly was a very important man and he owned the biggest house in Gum and it was called Gumbalding Manor. In fact, Mr Lordly owned most of that wood as well. Our part was only a little bit at the beginning. You knew when you were going into his part because there was a mossy track where Dad said carriages used to go pulled by horses and they were full of very posh people in their very best clothes. They were going to Gum Manor for a party.

That was in old Mr Lordly's day and his son was also called Mr Lordly – they called the old one Mr Lordly Senior so they could tell the difference. Anyway, it didn't matter to me because he was dead but what did matter was that his son, who was our Mr Lordly, did not want anybody going up the mossy track or crossing that track and going into his part of the wood. And just so that you could be sure of this there was a big sign that Mr Lordly got his workers to put up. It was on a big wooden stake that was hammered into the ground and a big notice was nailed across it. The notice was white and written on it in big red letters were the words 'Trespassers will be prosecuted' and once somebody was really prosecuted for trespassing.

My Uncle Sid said that a long time ago a person called Bill Lowe was prosecuted because he went into Mr Lordly's part of the woods and picked some daffodils that grew wild there. We had a girl called Doreen Lowe in our class and she was so gentle and frightened she would never do any harm. Bill was her granddad and I bet he was gentle and frightened and would never do anybody any harm either. Anyway, the story goes that when Mr Lordly was young he went out for a walk in his woods with his gun. He hadn't gone far when he saw quiet Bill Lowe just enjoying himself and picking a little bunch of daffs. Mr Lordly was angry and said that he was trespassing. And not long after that Bill got a summons and it said:

'Gerald Lordly, Esquire of the Manor, Gumbalding versus Bill Lowe of Cinder Cottage, Sunkstead'.

Poor Bill had to go to Hull assizes to hear all bad things said about him. He had only picked ten measly little daffodils for his pregnant wife and he had meant no harm. It wasn't as bad as when Charley stole my orange because the daffodils would flower again but Charley had actually eaten what he stole from me. Anyway, it was no good trying to talk to those men in court who just stared ahead and used the ten dead stolen daffodils in evidence against him – a withered brown bunch on a table for everybody to see. Mr Lordly hired some Big Boys who came from down south to do the prosecuting. But it turned out that the judge said they couldn't prosecute anybody for just for trespassing. I was very pleased to hear that from Uncle Sid and I hoped that was the end of that.

But it wasn't – the story didn't end there because when the Big Boys heard what the judge had to say they did not want to lose. And this was what they decided – the trespasser, Bill Lowe, had to pay for the daffodils that he had stolen. And so, Bill agreed because he was little and frightened in front of the big confident men. Anybody would know by looking at him that he would never do any harm but the Big Boys did not bother to look at him. Bill nodded his head fast and furious because if he didn't agree he might have to go to prison and what would his wife and children do then?

Mr Grey would have let poor Bill off, so long as he 'ran along' and agreed not to do it again. But Mrs Bantam would have said that there were consequences to your actions and you would have to pay. And now there was Bill shaking in his holey shoes because he knew that the judge and the Big Boys would say the same as Mrs Bantam.

Anyway, it was agreed by both sides that payment would be made for the daffodils. And poor Bill Trespasser gave a sigh of relief because he was going to walk free. And I can tell you I made a sigh of relief as well when Uncle Sid got to this part of story. But that was still not the end because then Mr Lordly was asked by the judge what he wanted to charge for his daffodils. Everybody thought that maybe a shilling would be about right and even though that was very expensive it would teach Bill a lesson and he would never pick daffodils in Mr Lordly's wood again. But then in a loud voice Mr Lordly replied.

"I charge half a crown." And there was a gasp in court — that was far too much for a bunch of ordinary wild daffodils, which, after all, were very small flowers and in any case, they were already dead. But there was more because Mr Lordly continued.

"I charge half a crown — for each daffodil." He smiled to himself and sat down and everybody thought that was unfair but the judge just nodded.

And that was a true story said my Uncle Sid and he would be right because he knew about all those sorts of things and he read *The Gazette* and the *Hull Daily Mail* and they told him everything that happened in these parts. All other grown-ups here read *News of the World* and that's not as serious, Mam said. And my dad said that the Big Boys would always take care of Mr Lordly and that poor Bill Trespasser had to pay. But he had not been able to pay all at once, of course, he would have to pay one penny a week for a long, long time. There were sad consequences for Bill's actions.

So, you can see why I was scared of Mr Lordly and even more scared of going into his wood and trespassing. But I did go in anyway because I liked it so much in there. I was always very, very careful indeed not to be seen by Mr Lordly. I hid behind tree trunks and when I went across that mossy track I bent double and dodged in the shady patches. And of course, I never ever picked daffodils – oh yes, they were still there because Bill Lowe didn't dig them up he only picked flowers and as everybody knows they flower again next year. So, I could still look at them shaking their heads at me warning me to be careful and to never steal them, and I never did.

But in a way, there was something that I did steal from Mr Lordly. Because, you see, the woodland scenes went straight into my head along with the birds and the bees already buzzing there. I could see lovely trees reaching to the sky and that little mossy track with the sun shining through in patches. I could see it at any time in my head. And whenever I wanted I could be in the woods again even if I was in bossy Mrs Bantam's class trying to do sums and spellings. And I didn't think anybody could take you to court for sights that you steal and keep in your head. But I didn't tell anybody about it just in case I had to pay like poor Bill. And I didn't tell anybody that I often went into Mr Lordly's woods either.

Sometimes I went on my own and sometimes all us kids went in and trespassed. Our Gwendy came and Terry of course and sometimes we even took his little brother Stewy. Once we had a game of dare to see who could get farthest up that mossy track. We went creeping under cover of trees and grass and it was scary in case of any consequences but we wanted to see who was bravest and so we crept on and on. And that's when we saw a big wooden shed nearly hidden by undergrowth. Terry got right up to it, he was always the bravest. It was great fun but

115

then we looked up and saw that we were very near the great Manor House where Mr Lordly lived and he could be standing there looking out of his window at us that very minute. We suddenly got very scared that he would come after us with his gun and we stood still not daring to move.

"Let's go," Stewy shouted into the silence and it was as if somebody had really pressed a trigger because we all turned and ran and ran. We didn't stop but we hurtled back to our house with twigs and branches all cracking like shots under our feet.

Later I thought about that shed for a long time and wondered what was in it. Then one day I was off school with a cough and I was allowed outside because Mam agreed with Miss Hart and she thought fresh air would do me good. So, I wandered about on my own until I came to the woods and I couldn't help going down that track again. I bent double and dodged in the tree shadows of course. My heart was hammering away in case of guns and Mr Lordly and his Big Boys. But was careful and I kept out of the bright splashes of sunlight and kept to the dark patches on the mossy track and soon I was right up to the big shed. Then I forgot all about Mr Lordly for a few minutes and I put my hands on the rough wooden sides of the shed and pressed my eye to see through a crack. And I was amazed because I could see an old-fashioned carriage with its red shafts for a horse and red velvet seats and I could see brass carriage lamps on the side. It was a bit like the trap that Brenda's horse, Lucky Basket, pulled. But Brenda's trap was tiny and black all over and this one was huge and bright red inside. I stared at it for a long time remembering what Dad said about carriages driving along the mossy track to the Manor House. I thought of rich Mr Lordly Senior with his posh friends who could afford to sit in a red velvet carriage and ride up the mossy track to a big party. And I thought about poor Bill Lowe I felt very sad.

Then something even sadder happened because it happened to me – not in our woods but at school. Brenda and most of my class went up into the next class but I had to stay behind because, as you know, I was not very good at sums and spelling. That was the consequence for not learning what I should have been learning at school. I had to stay in bossy Mrs Bantam's class and that was a sad thing for me. Charley stayed behind with me but he didn't care he just laughed. Doreen Lowe stayed with me as well but she just gave a little frightened smile. Then all younger children came up from The Huts and all the same lessons of sums and spelling that I had heard already started again. It was boring as well as sad.

Then one day, much to my surprise, something very interesting happened in class and it cheered me up. You see, Mrs Bantam wanted us all to enter a painting competition for a garden party at Gumbalding Manor. We had done a lot of painting with Mr Grey but we never painted with Mrs Bantam, she always did sums and spelling. So, this was very unusual.

"Now listen carefully, children. *The Gazette* is sponsoring this competition so there will be certificates for the lucky winners at a Garden Party. The title of the painting is 'Glades', which has been chosen especially by Mr Lordly." Well, we didn't know what she meant by glades and so we all just sat still and stared at her. Then she got us organised and all our desks were covered with newspaper and white painting paper was given out and then powder paint was scooped into little white saucers. There was silence and we all sat very still till Charley burst out laughing. He had got the *News of the World* newspaper and there was a bare lady on it. Mrs Bantam sent him out of class to stand near the dripping taps again.

"Charley Fox, as a punishment you will enter this prestigious competition in your own time and learn some extra spellings as a consequence of your bad behaviour," she bossed. Charley went out grinning he never bothered about consequences. And still we all waited. We didn't know what to paint. What was 'Glades'?

"Now, children, you will all be familiar with glades in our woodlands. Where there is a little clearing or a little path there will be a glade with dappled sunshine." Ah, at last now I knew what she meant. I grabbed my brush and started – and I just could not stop. I painted that little mossy track with my dad's tree standing proud and unbending and my mam with her sewn-on leaves and then Uncle Sid standing up straight up looking out and seeing everything that went on above us all. Aunty Vera was in her pretty dress and she was dancing all over the place. Sunshine tried to get through all the leaves but it only managed it in a few places. I dabbed spatters of white in the darkness of the moss. I knew every bit of that scene. I could see it as clearly as if I had been standing there. I worked all afternoon and I didn't even have to think.

"Well done, that is truly excellent – I had no idea you that could paint so well," that was Mrs Bantam and she said 'well done' to me for first time ever. But I hadn't quite finished. I got some yellow paint and right at the front I painted ten little daffodils just to show everybody that Bill Lowe didn't do any real harm. Then when I looked up Doreen was staring at my painting then she looked at me and gave me a very big smile, not a weak little one like she usually did – it was a great big wide smile which turned into a laugh. So, she knew that story and she knew why I had put the daffodils there.

I went to the garden party at Gumbalding Manor with Mam and Gwendy. Me and Gwendy were all dressed up in some dresses Mam had made especially for this prestigious time. Mam was in her best costume with her matching best shoes and handbag. And she said that if Mr Lordly spoke to us we had to call him 'Sir'. Dad didn't come of course, he said that he was too busy getting on with looking after the animals on our farm. But I thought it was because he never liked anything too posh and that was why he didn't like getting dressed in his best clothes. He was much happier working on our farm at Gum which was, after all, our livelihood. And even though Mam got his black suit out and brushed it down he would not change his mind. So, we went without him.

There was a big tent on the lawn and trestles with white cloths and little cakes to eat and little cups of tea filled from big brown teapots. Sir Mr Lordly was standing at the door of his

Manor with his hands behind his back. And do you know he was very old and very little and there was no gun in sight. I was surprised to see that he was a very old little man and even had a bald head. He didn't look very frightening at all I didn't know how I could ever have been scared of him. And I couldn't help but notice that he was on his own and he didn't seem to have any friends at all. It was only his hired caterers in their little black and white outfits that spoke to him.

After our tea and cakes we went into the tent and looked round. There were jam pots and sponge cakes and flowers – so many people had sent things to be judged by Mr Lordly who had given certificates to say where they had come in the competition. Mam couldn't wait to find my entry and to our surprise there were loads of paintings all pinned up and it took ages to find mine. But when we did we were so excited because it said First Prize. There was a comment underneath, it said 'This is a very realistic painting' and Mr Lordly had written it. Well of course it was – it was that scene from his own woods that I had stolen. I didn't say anything about that though, just in case of consequences.

So of course, my mam didn't know what I had done and she couldn't have been more pleased with me. She pulled her stomach in, pushed her shoulders back and held her head up and smiled a beautiful smile at everybody. Then Mr Lordly came to present the prizes and he gave me a big certificate with '*The Gazette Painting Competition* – First Prize' written on it in big red letters. Then I had a big tin of sweets, 'With compliments of *The Gazette*' it said. And then if that was not enough, Mr Lordly ruffled my fine hair and took half a crown out of his own pocket and gave it to me. Well, I was so taken aback that I forgot to say 'thank you' never mind 'Sir'. I had never had so many sweets or as much money in one go, in all my life. I was thinking that I could keep that money in my secret place in-between my mattresses with my charm bracelet until our next Sunday school trip. Then I would have as much money to spend as Suzy.

Suddenly I felt as tall as the tallest tree in the woods and I felt as if I could do anything. I had won first prize for my painting, I had a bag of sweets and I had some money and my mam was pleased with me. In fact, I felt so good that I went round and gave a sweet to all the little kids near me. I gave Doreen two and she laughed out loud. I was so happy.

And it was a funny thing but after winning first prize for my painting I tried harder at school and even when I was poorly I learnt my spellings in bed. Then I started to get better marks and then I worked a bit harder and got even better. I didn't get ten out of ten, mind you, because I had a long way to go from nought and so I couldn't put sums and spelling on my 'What I am good at' list. But I didn't mind too much because I could definitely put – good at painting – on my list. And another good thing was that I started not to mind spellings and sums being in my head any more. They lived there now quite nicely with birds and bees and glades. And of course, I was not so scared of Mr Lordly after I had seen that he was such a little old man.

Then the next thing we knew was that Mr Lordly was dead. Uncle Sid read it in *The Gazette* that he had crossed over. He had been dead in his bed for two days and was only found by his old housekeeper when she got back after her weekend off. So, his Big Boys didn't take care of him at the end.

There was a very big funeral; everybody came to pay their respects to the important Mr Gerald Lordly Esquire and some people even came from down south. I thought it was very surprising that he had so many friends now he had died but there was nobody to bother to see if he was alright at the weekend when he was crossing over. Anyway, Gum Church was packed out and some people were even standing outside. Uncle Sid went but my dad didn't, even though Mam had got his funeral suit out of their wardrobe and brushed it down again. Of course, he said he was too busy looking after our farm animals.

Then after all that fuss of the funeral the estate had to be cleared and us kids crept up the mossy track. I suppose that as Mr Lordly was dead we could have gone there without hiding but we were still careful because you just never knew what the consequences would be if we were found out. So, we watched from the shadows, all the workers were cutting down undergrowth near the big house. It was in a real mess. The house was practically in ruins inside, so they said, and the garden was covered in tall grasses and overhanging trees. They lit big bonfires to get rid of all that rubbish and we watched as smoke climbed into the sky. Then all at once a wind got up from nowhere and we saw flames bend and turn sideways. A great big red flash roared up to the old wooden coach shed and we heard a bang. We were scared then even though we knew it could not be Mr Lordly with his gun and we ran off home. Then we heard the fire engine bell but we knew it was too late to save the shed. So it was all over.

But a few days later I found out that it wasn't all quite over as I had thought. You see, the village Bobby from Ringam came riding down on our lane on his bike. He saw us kids playing and came over to us. He wanted to know if we had ever been up that mossy track in the woods and of course we all just stood there not daring to say anything. I started to think about trespassing and consequences. I licked my lips and went very red. The Bobby saw me of course and he took me to one side away from the others.

"Can you remember things in your head?" he asked bending down to look into my eyes. I nodded. I was too frightened to speak. My face went redder and my mouth went drier. That was it then – he had come to take me to Hull assizes like Bill Lowe. I didn't know how he had found out that I had stolen Mr Lordly's glades scene and kept it in my head and used it for the painting competition. But somehow, he had and I would have to face the consequences and pay. I would have to give that half a crown back and my First Prize certificate. The Bobby from Ringam could take me away straight to prison and he could shout the bad news like Posty, as he pedalled on his way with me on the crossbar of his bike.

'She's arrested, she's guilty.'

But he didn't do that, instead he kept looking into my eyes. "Did you see what was inside the shed?" I nodded. He had found a second crime and I was going to have to pay for looking into the shed as well. I could be paying all my life and now that I had been found out, there was no point in lying. I admitted everything there and then and told him all about my painting and all about the lovely carriage with the red velvet seats and brass carriage lamps. Funnily enough though, he didn't bother at all about my painting he was just interested in the carriage that had been burnt. He said that he was pleased with me because they needed to know what was in the shed for insurance purposes and I had been very helpful. So that really was the end of that. And he just said, "Now run along and play," so I did and I didn't have to pay and there were no sad consequences for me that time.

Chapter 11

Saturdays

There was no more painting for me after that Glades competition at Gum Manor. In fact, we never did painting again in Mrs Bantam's class. You see, Mrs Bantam made us work harder at sums and spellings and there wasn't time for anything else now. There was never a minute to spare with all the hard work, so I was always glad when it was Friday night and I didn't have to go to school on Saturday and I could have fun.

Saturdays were really good at our house. For one thing, I didn't have to get up early to catch our school bus and for another you could do what you wanted. The first thing I did when I finally got up was to listen to the wireless, there was a programme of children's songs on and I loved them. I used to sit at our table and listen and sometimes I turned the volume up to hear the tunes better and hear their dancing notes but when my dad came in for a sit down and a mug of tea there had to be no noise. He wanted everything quiet so that he could have his tea and a have rest in peace.

"Stop that noise," he said and so the wireless had to be turned off. And it didn't go back on because Dad and me went to Ringam after his mug of tea.

Dad drove as if there wasn't a minute to lose. Well, I suppose that every minute away from our farm was a minute lost for him – he always worked so hard for our livelihood.

At last we pulled up with a jerk in the market place in Ringam and hurriedly jumped out to get a list of things from the chemist because Aunty Vera had got a new baby girl. Aunty Vera was so pleased to have a little baby girl. It was not at all like when I was born. I was the third girl and my mam and dad quite naturally would have wanted a boy after having two girls. You just knew that Mam and Dad would not be pleased to have a third girl when a boy could have worked on our farm. But it was different for Aunty Vera because she already had two boys and so when her little girl arrived it was a wonderful treat for her and Uncle Sid.

Anyway, back to our shopping and next we had to go to the grocers to pick up bread and papers for everybody. We girls always got three comics as well – one for each of us and we had a bag of boiled sweets each. That was another good thing about Saturday – it was the one day of the week we got sweets and comics and after that our van jogged us back home. Then I had the rest of the day to please myself.

Sometimes on Saturdays I played with Brenda and we had great fun. We were still friends, you see, even though Brenda was now in the next class up from me. And if I wasn't with Brenda, I played with our Gwendy or my cousins Terry and Stewy from next door.

Terry had just invented a new game for Saturdays when we had nothing else to do. You needed plenty of time for this game because there was a lot of waiting. It was on our railway line. Down our lane just past our Hoss Paster field there was a level crossing and that's where we played. We knew that you weren't supposed to be on the railway line because the trains were so heavy that they couldn't stop in time even if they saw you. But Terry knew what to do. He said that you could listen out for trains by lying down and putting your head on the rail. He said that if your ear was on the metal then you could hear a train coming even when it was a mile away and there would be plenty of time for us to run before it got to us. So, after listening with our heads down and we were sure that it was clear, we got on with our game.

First Terry wanted to put a penny on the track and we had to find a good place for it to go. Then we went to sit on top of one of the big white railway gates at the level crossing and waited for the next train. The idea was that the engine could squash Terry's penny flat.

Suddenly there it was, the big train coming in a black cloud, out of nowhere – a big engine with the driver peering out through a lot of smoke. Of course, he couldn't see Terry's penny and he always smiled and waved and we always waved back. We waved and waved with our arms outstretched as the train and carriages or trucks chugged on their way to Ringam station where they left coal or goods for farmers to pick up. In summer, there were passenger carriages full of families with kids going to spend all day at Ripsea seaside.

But we couldn't wait all day to see what had happened to Terry's penny, we were so excited so we waved more frantically hoping that we could make the train go faster and disappear more quickly. But instead, I was sure that it slowed down with its carriages creeping round the next bend making us wait even longer. Then at last we saw the back of the final carriage fading from our view and there was nothing more to be seen except the smoke. We jumped off the gate and dashed onto the railway line to find Terry's penny and see if it was squashed. It was! It was completely splattered with the King's head spread out all over. I tried it with my farthing from my charm bracelet but it was no good and I just found it pushed off line and into the cinders. I thought about us kids with our heads on the line listening for a train, and if Terry was wrong about hearing the train a mile away our heads could be squashed and spread out just like his penny or pushed in the cinders like my farthing. It was a dangerous game and we loved it because of the fear which was a fun sort of fear.

My mam kept warning us that it was no place for children to play but we took no notice; it was too much fun. It was like the woods where we played even though we knew that we should not be trespassing. And just like the woods we made sure that nobody ever saw us on the railway line. Of course, there were lots of signs just like Mr Lordly's to say that you shouldn't be there. But this time they were not in clear red writing on white board, they were metal signs with hundreds of bobbly black letters and they were badly worn in places so you could hardly read them. You could just make out words like – 'danger' and 'trespassers' and at the end it said 'by order' and there was a squiggly signature so we knew it was serious but it just made it more fun. We always sat on a big white gate watching and waiting for the train to come and splatter Terry's pennies, every Saturday.

There were two gates at our level crossing one on each side and Uncle Sid said that they had to be closed 'at all times' so that nothing and nobody could get onto the rail and be in danger of accidentally being squashed by a train. So, the gates were always closed but it didn't matter to us of course because we just climbed over them.

Then one day more big signs were put up by some rail workers, right next to each gate and this time you could read the writing because they were new signs. Uncle Sid said that they were for people who were driving across the line, 'Please open far gate before crossing' they said. Of course, us kids fell about laughing because it didn't make sense. You had to cross the railway line to open the far gate. How could you open the far gate if you didn't cross the line? Anyway, we carried on playing our game and soon forgot all about the new notice. It was always great fun and Saturdays went on like they always had until I did something that changed my Saturdays forever.

I decided that I wanted to learn to play our piano. Mam could play and if she wasn't at her sewing machine she used to play the piano at night. I used to listen to her when I was in bed and I could hear the piano notes dancing up our stairs and into our bedroom. They played about on my bed till they got slower and slower and quieter and quieter and they gently fell asleep with me.

Our Gwendy had been having piano lessons for ages and she could play really well. It looked so easy to do and I wanted to play tunes and make the notes dance around. Just think, if I could play the piano I could play tunes any time I wanted and I wouldn't have to wait for Saturdays on the wireless or the nights when Mam played the piano. So, I set about my task and tried the notes but the tunes were just not there. Then Dad came in for his mug of tea and a rest.

"Stop that awful noise," he would say because he wanted some peace and quiet before he went outside to work on our farm again. So, I shut our piano lid till he'd gone and then I crept back in and started again but it was no good, he was right it was an awful noise. I could not make the notes dance. So, Mam said I had better go for some lessons.

She arranged for me to go to Sunkstead on the bus every Saturday morning for my piano lesson. I missed my children's wireless programme and then I missed playing about on our railway line trying to squash our coins, because when I got back from my music lesson the first trains had gone through and all the kids had got fed up with the railway line game and they were waiting for dinnertime. So, I had to give up trying to get my farthing squashed flat and concentrate on my piano playing instead.

My teacher was called Mrs Treasure and Mam said that she was a treasure because she was a very good music teacher. But she couldn't teach me. Every week after I had tried my best she wrote about my progress in a little book that I took home for my mam to read. And Mam was always waiting to see what it said.

'Has not yet achieved the essential skill of hand /eye coordination ...' read Mam, which meant that I was no good at playing the piano. So, I had to practise even more and then go off to catch the bus to Sunkstead again the next Saturday. This went on for ages and my little book was nearly full and still it said that I could not play the tunes. Well, I knew that and so did Mam, the notes would simply not get together and do a little dance. It got me down a bit.

Then one day after my lesson, Freddy Lowe was waiting at the bus stop at Sunkstead. I had seen him before because he was Doreen's dad. And as it turned out he had got a job on a farm right down our lane over our railway line and miles on past our Far Side and Bottom Field. He was very pleased because it was extra money and there was a little house for his family down there and he could keep on with his milking job at a Sunkstead farm in the morning and at night. And as we stood there waiting for the bus he whistled some tunes and he was a good whistler and you could hear the notes dancing about and they danced all over the bus when we got on and everybody smiled.

Not long after that Freddy moved into his little cottage with his wife and their four kids. He had bought an old pickup truck and it came chugging along with their brightly painted furniture rattling about in the back making such a noise. Doreen and her little brother and sisters were sitting with the furniture and they waved and shouted out as they passed us. We were all watching standing in our lane and we waved back.

"Good luck to you all, Freddy," shouted Aunty Vera and they laughed and waved even more with their arms outstretched till their truck disappeared down our lane.

Every morning Doreen had to walk past our fields and the drain, then on over our level crossing and up our lane to wait for our school bus. It took her an hour she said, but she didn't seem to mind. Our bus stop was getting crowded now – there was our Katy going to the High School at Ripsea and a little gang of five going to Ringam Primary School. There was me, our Gwendy, Terry and his little brother Stewy, who had just started school. And now there was Doreen as well. We stood there in all weathers at our lane end on a little patch of grass on the roadside that we had worn to bare soil, waiting for our bus every day. One day when a cold east wind got up we hunched under the hoods of our macs.

"My dad says when things get bad just whistle," shouted Doreen above the howling wind. And she started her tune – then we all joined in and we tried to whistle our way through our favourite tunes that we had heard on the wireless and we weren't very good but our brave notes tumbled about in the wind. And before we knew it we could see our bus suddenly coming out of nowhere trundling on its way to pick us up. And just as I got on the bus I saw Freddy Lowe in his old truck coming from his milking job at Sunkstead and going to work on the farm down our lane.

Sometimes at night, I stood on our windowsill and saw his truck again rattling to Sunkstead for evening milking and then an hour or two later I heard him rattling back down our lane to his cottage. Mrs Lowe got a cleaning job in Ringam and on Saturday mornings when I went to my music lesson she was walking up our lane. Doreen had to look after her brother and sisters while her Mam walked to Ringam to work. She walked so that she didn't have to spend hard earned money on bus fares.

'Good expression,' wrote Mrs Treasure in my little book one Saturday, 'but...' and she would write things that I was still doing wrong as I kept on playing my stiff notes. Then one day at home a tiny tune crept out as I practised – it just came unexpectedly from nowhere and the notes started dancing. It was only a little stumbling dance but when Aunty Vera came in wearing her pretty dress and her best strappy shoes she took the notes and danced them all over our room. Next Saturday Mrs Treasure wrote 'Good progress', and the next thing I knew was that she had rung Mam to say that I was good enough to take my first music exam. Mrs Treasure was a treasure after all, my mam had been right.

On the day of my exam Mam took me to Hull on the bus and we walked to a street with some tall buildings with big doors. We were in posh streets here with no bomb rubble in sight. We timidly went through one of the doors with a brass handle and we sat down on a polished wooden bench. It was dark and cold and I was suddenly full of fear and it was not the fun fear of playing on our railway line it was a really frightening fear. I felt like Terry's penny must have felt when it was waiting on the railway line to be squashed flat. Then I remembered what Doreen had said about whistling and I tried to blow through the gap in my two front teeth and the notes tumbled bravely about. Then after a long wait it was time to go through into another room on my own and try the exam.

"Let us commence," said the examiner looking at me without any expression at all and he sat back with his arms folded while I played the pieces that I had practised for so long. I didn't know if they danced, I was too frightened to listen.

"Thank you, my dear, that will be all." He looked up and he smiled a flat smile and then started writing in his notebook. I shuffled out.

"Did you do well?" asked Mam anxiously; she had been spending money on my music lessons with Mrs Treasure and of course it must not be wasted.

"I don't know." And I really did not know and I kept going over and over all the notes in my head to see if I had played them in the right order, but I couldn't remember. Then the next Saturday night something awful happened that put my music exam right out of my head.

Our Gwendy and me were in bed listening to Mam playing the piano and the notes danced up our stairs and into our bedroom and onto our beds as they usually did. We ate our Saturday boiled sweets – and read our comics enjoying every minute. Then that awful thing happened.

First, we heard some racing footsteps pounding through darkness outside below our bedroom window.

"Help – somebody. Help, for God's sake help." I looked at Gwendy with startled eyes and she stared back at me unblinking. Then quick as a flash we jumped out of our beds and stood on our windowsill to peer into darkness. We could just make out our train driver as he charged past and then we heard him bang our door open.

"Help! Help! I've squashed a man flat – flattened his truck with him in it." There was a long silence as our Gwendy and me listened with hammering hearts holding our breath not daring to breathe. Mam stopped playing the piano and the last lonely note stopped dancing and dropped dead on my bed.

"Ring for ambulance, doctor, fire engine and police – get the whole bloody lot – I've splattered him. For God's sake…"

We heard Mam take charge and rush next door to ring up on Grandma's phone and then there was silence. The next thing we heard was Aunty Vera's darting steps as she shot out into the night with the folds of her pretty afternoon frock flying after her.

"Hang on, just hang, Freddy, I've got some water," she ran screaming, with a pint mug so full, that water was spilling everywhere. She had a wet dish cloth in her other hand and she hadn't even stopped to change out of her best strappy shoes, she stumbled and nearly fell over, so she kicked them off and ran down our muddy lane barefoot. We watched her flailing outline till she was just a black shadow.

"Hang on, Freddy," her voice was snatched into a deathly darkness and I knew that Freddy could not hear her. The little baby girl shrieked next door in her cot.

My stale sweet stuck to roof of my mouth and I spat it out onto my comic.

Next, we saw everybody – Uncle Sid, my dad, my mam, the engine driver and even our Katy running. And Uncle Sid was shouting that they needed to lift the van off Freddy's body. It would be no use I knew he would be flattened and his head splattered on the rails like Terry's penny.

We heard Grandma shushing the baby then there was nothing. Our Gwendy and me breathed the trembling breath that we had been holding in for so long. Then the fear came rushing in me and it was a terrifying fear that was beyond the fun fear of our railway game and way beyond the frightening fear of my music exam. It was a deadly fear like my operation fear. I crept into Gwendy's bed holding onto my charm bracelet with my farthing that had not been squashed. Then we waited and for ages and ages there was nothing but our thoughts willing 'please somebody come, please come and help, please, please' I forced my mind to concentrate to bring that help quickly and for Freddy to hang on if it wasn't already too late. Then at last we heard them – vehicles speeding down lane one after another and another, after another. Help had come and we fell into a nightmare sleep.

In the morning, I went down and saw Mam and Dad still in last night's clothes sitting by the fire with our black kettle boiling and whistling its high-pitched tune. Mam and Dad sat there not moving just feeling the pain. They were covered from head to foot with black smoke and dirt. Aunty Vera came in quietly and just stood with us, she still had no shoes on and her feet were thick with mud – her lovely flowery frock was covered in blood, and tears were rolling down her face. She said nothing.

"Poor old Freddy," said my dad at last and I was glad somebody had said something because I didn't know what to do. Our kettle whistled some more and the notes clashed together fiercely. Then Dad took it off the fire and put it on the side so the notes crashed to the floor. There was peace and quiet at last, but Dad didn't even have his mug of tea before he went out to see to his animals. Aunty Vera went back next-door and Mam told us to go and have our bath and then get dressed because it was Sunday and we still had to go to Ringam to Sunday school and chapel.

There was no Doreen at our bus stop that Monday and she never came and stood there on our little patch of soil ever again. It was such bad news and even though Posty, our postman liked bad news, he did not like this. He didn't shout anything about Freddy when he was on his rounds of the villages. So, at school us kids told everybody and they were all very shocked. But next day everything was back to normal.

Well, it was back to normal for us but not for Freddy's family. Freddy did not die but he was in hospital for ages and came out with a broken body. There was only his head that hadn't needed an operation because it was the only bit that had not been squashed flat or hit by clashing metal. His head had not had a hit thank goodness it had been like my farthing and just got pushed into the cinders.

And now I knew what the notice 'Please open far gate before crossing' meant and it was not so funny after all. You see, Freddy had come home late from working on the Sunkstead farm in his old truck and he must have opened the near gate then driven onto our railway line. Then leaving his truck on the line he got out to open the far gate. And there was a train coming and when he got back in his truck he was squashed flat. Our strong east wind was howling and Freddy would not have heard the train. The engine driver couldn't have seen the truck because it was dark and he couldn't have stopped in time in any case. It was nobody's fault just an awful accident. And that was more or less the end of Freddy. He would never work on a farm again said Dad.

Except that Freddy had other ideas, and he tried so hard to get better. He walked with crutches up and down our lane day after day and he didn't give up. I heard him whistling while he exercised up and down and his whistle got stronger and so did his legs.

But he didn't get strong enough to do farm work and after a few months he had to move because my dad was right, he would never work on a farm again. He had to get out of the cottage to make room for the next farmer and one day we heard a friend with a van coming to take Freddy's little family away with their few sticks of furniture. We all watched as they went past.

"Good luck to you all," shouted Aunty Vera but they didn't take any notice. Mrs Lowe was looking down and the kids were silent as the van sloped quietly past. Mr Lowe was looking straight ahead.

Doreen came back to school after a few weeks but I never said anything to her about the accident. Then after a long time I went with Dad to collect some coal from Ringam station yard. Dad was shovelling when I heard it. It was a faint whistling coming from the far end of platform. It got louder and louder and the notes from the tune came dancing round me. I didn't need to look up because I knew who it was. Nobody could whistle like him.

Freddy told us that he was now a part-time ticket collector and Mrs Lowe kept the place clean and they had managed to rent a little cottage in Ringam. So, that was good news for them at last. Oh, and I nearly forgot, there was good news for me as well. I passed my music exam. So – playing the piano – went on my 'What I am good at' list. And just one more thing, after the accident some men came and put up another notice on our railway line side, as if we didn't have enough. But this time it was way down the line just near the bend. It was for the engine drivers to read. 'WHISTLE' it said, just that, in great big letters. And that's what the trains always did from then on when they were coming up to our level crossing, so that nobody would get flattened by a train ever again. Everybody could hear the train and get clear in time, thank goodness.

And when Dad came in for his mug of tea we often heard the trains go past on the railway line and they always whistled a tune – it was so loud that it travelled right up our lane to our house. The notes didn't dance but they were not meant to they just shrieked their warning round and round our room. You would think that they would have disturbed Dad's peace and quiet but he never ever said anything at all against them.

Chapter 12

Scotland

My dad always said that if you waited long enough you got used to things that you didn't like but I was not sure that it was a true saying. You see, I never got used to staying behind in Mrs Bantam's class and so I was very pleased that after my good news about passing my music exam there was some more good news for me. I went up into the next class at last. Mam was very pleased with me because you were not going to get on in the world if you were stuck behind in a class with kids younger than you. Mrs Bossy Bantam had finally got me to do better with my school work but that wasn't the reason that I went up. All the kids that had stayed behind had to go up because there was no more room and our class had got too big. I didn't tell Mam that the others were coming with me though, because she might not have been as pleased. Apart from pleasing my mam there was another good thing about going up and it was that I could be with Brenda again. I went straight to sit with her in my new class and she had saved me a seat next to her all that time when I had stayed behind. My new teacher was called Miss McBride and she was pleased with me as well because I was still making progress. A new girl called Melanie had taken my place near the bottom of the class along with Charley and Doreen.

Melanie had just started in Miss McBride's class like me, but she was also new to our school. Melanie and her mam had moved to Ringam from Hull and the funny thing was she had no dad and there never had been any dad because her mam was called Miss Pratt not Mrs Pratt.

And because there was no dad, Miss Pratt had to go to work. She went to Hull every morning just like Aunty Peggy did. When we got off our bus at Ringam to go to school we saw her on the other side of the road waiting in her high heeled shoes for the bus to Hull.

Brenda said that her mam had told her that Melanie was an American war baby. She said that a lot of American soldiers came over here in the war and they were very handsome and knew all sorts of exciting things. Miss Pratt did not stick with the lads that she knew from the village but went off with the American soldiers and she fell in love with one them. But he had to go away to fight and was never heard of again. Then nine months later Melanie was born and that's how she had no dad. I asked Mam if she could tell me any more about it all but she was too busy making apple pie. She made lovely apple pies and she was in a hurry because she had to go out and help Dad with milking our cows. Mam was always in a hurry what with housework and sewing and farm work. But as she put the pie in the oven she did say that it was a shameful affair and she looked sad. Other people must have thought the same because I couldn't help but notice that Miss Pratt did not have any friends.

Melanie didn't have any friends at school either and was always on her own even though she was very pretty and you could see she was going to be beautiful like her mam. But Melanie didn't seem to want friends and she didn't take much notice of anybody – even our teacher, Miss McBride – she just stared into space with a faraway look in her eyes as if she didn't want to be there. At playtime, she stood waiting for the whistle to go then when we were back in our classroom she was always staring out of the window. Our windows were high up so you couldn't see much but Melanie lifted her head and just looked at the sky with that sad faraway look in her eyes.

"Now, children, our lesson is about Scotland today," said Miss McBride with that funny twang of hers in her voice. She talked like that because she was from Scotland and we couldn't always understand what she was saying.

"This is a picture of a mountain in Scotland, I don't suppose any of you have seen a mountain," she held up the picture for us and even Melanie looked at it – and it was true we had never seen anything like it in our lives because our land here was as flat as my mam's pastry when she rolled it to make us apple pie. I had seen a few hills of course when we went on our Sunday school trip to Scarborough but these mountains were something very different.

I stared at that picture with the rocks reaching to the sky and I remembered that other saying of my dad's that it was better to stick to what you knew, just to be on the safe side. If Melanie's mam had stuck to who she knew then there wouldn't have been a shameful affair and she would have been married ages ago to one of our local lads. But that mountain did look very exciting and I could see that Melanie couldn't take her eyes off it – maybe she would like to escape to a place like Scotland because she just couldn't seem to get used to being stuck with us at our school in Ringam.

Then one day Melanie didn't come to school. She was away for days on end. We saw her mam, Miss Pratt in her high heels, waiting for the bus to take her to work in Hull like she always did. But Melanie didn't come to school and Mr Bantam our Headmaster asked if anybody had seen her playing out. Nobody knew anything because she never played with any of us kids anyway.

Charley knew where she was though. At playtime, he told us that when Melanie's mam went to catch the bus, Melanie stayed in her house all day. He had seen her looking from behind the curtains when he came past to school. Anyway, nobody told Mr Bantam but the next thing we heard was that the Kid Catcher had been sent for. We were very scared of the Kid Catcher. Mam told us that if you didn't go to school he came round to your house to make you go. He must have done his job with Melanie because next day Miss Pratt and Melanie came across our playground in a hurry. We all crowded round to see what was going to happen.

Miss Pratt pushed through the crowd with her head held high and her tight rolled curls bobbing up and down as she walked towards Mr Bantam who was coming across our playground to meet her.

"Melanie doesn't want to come to school, she doesn't want to be here," said Miss Pratt as she tossed her curls even more.

"She must come to school; that is the Law, she has no choice in the matter," said Mr Bantam quietly. But Miss Pratt tossed her head of tight curls again and kept on walking with her high heels tap-tapping on the hard playground. Then they went into Mr Bantam's office and his door was shut behind them so we couldn't hear what they said any more.

We all had to go to lessons because the whistle went, but the next thing we saw was Miss Pratt walking off across our playground as quietly and sensibly as if she had serviceable shoes on like mine. Then Melanie crept back into our class and sat down with that sad faraway look in her eyes. She really was stuck with us kids and Ringam School whether she liked it or not.

When I got home that night I told my dad what had happened. He just said that Melanie would soon get used to us all and get used to Ringham School as well. But I never thought that Melanie would get used to us because she always looked so sad.

Then a bit later on it happened again. Melanie didn't come to school and I thought she was up to her old tricks. But then I realised that this was different because Miss Pratt wasn't waiting at the bus stop either.

Charley told us all that he had looked through the window of their house and it was empty – there was nothing at all inside – no Melanie, no Miss Pratt and no furniture. Nobody knew where they had gone but Melanie never came back to our school again and Miss Pratt never stood at the bus stop in her high heel shoes again. It was all we talked about that day as we wondered where they had gone. I thought that maybe they had gone to see the mountains in Scotland and funnily enough I found out later that my dad and Uncle Sid were going to Scotland. It was so exciting.

My dad was not excited about going away though. It was the first time I could remember him going out of East Yorkshire and he was not too keen. In fact, he was only going because he had heard that you could buy good, cheap sheep there.

Our car would have to be filled to the brim with petrol because they were going miles away and up The Great North Road. According to Uncle Sid there were loads of mountains covered with sheep in Scotland and the sheep were just waiting to be brought back here to Gum. The idea was that they could make a good profit from them because we couldn't buy sheep here at such low prices. Dad was looking sad when the day came because even though he wanted to make money for our farm, he loved Gum where the land was as flat as Mam's rolled pastry for apple pies. And that was another thing – he was used to eating Mam's cooking – especially her apple pie. There wouldn't be any of that in Scotland and I didn't think that he would get used to their food.

When the big day came at last, Dad and Uncle Sid were dressed up in their smart sports jackets and grey flannel trousers. They both had new top coats as well because it was apparently cold up there. At last my dad put his best trilby hat on and rushed to get to our car.

"Come on let's get going," he said. "The sooner we get there, the sooner we can get back."

Uncle Sid couldn't wait to get going either but for a different reason, he thought that it would be exciting and he was going to do all the driving because he loved driving. He gave Aunty Vera a big kiss on her lips and Aunty Vera laughed as he bounced into the car.

Dad slid into the passenger seat without kissing Mam and he just stared ahead. Uncle Sid revved the engine and grinned then off they went with Dad not looking sideways but staring straight ahead as if he could make the car get there faster and get back to Gum sooner if he concentrated. Uncle Sid waved through the open side window while we all stood in our lane and waved with our arms outstretched. We watched the car and

Uncle Sid's hand as he kept on waving. Mam waved and I saw her lift her head to the horizon and up to the sky and then a sad look come into her eyes, it was that faraway look that I had seen in Melanie's eyes.

"Have a good time," shouted Aunty Vera. Her pretty frock was pressed up to her body showing up her lovely figure. My mam had a lovely figure as well but she still had her pinny on so you couldn't see it and anyway she soon dashed back inside to finish her baking.

Aunty Vera stayed with us for another minute as we all waved and waved, full of excitement till we saw our little black car turn onto the main road at our lane end. We saw it chugging along taking my dad and Uncle Sid off to Scotland. We jumped up and down to see over the hedges and catch a last sight of that speck of a car. Then suddenly it went round a corner and over the horizon at Sunkstead and was gone. For a minute, we were shocked – our dads had gone and we couldn't believe it and we all stood staring at an empty road.

Then Aunty Vera's laugh broke into our heads. "Don't forget we're going to Hull Fair tonight." And then off she ran gathering up the folds of her frock in a hurry to get on with her work.

"You'll need to wear your school shoes tonight that clay road to Hull Fair will be filthy with all those people churning up the mud," said Mam dishing up our tea. I had hoped to wear my best shoes but there was no changing Mam's mind. I had to go in my serviceable school shoes and that was that.

Then, when it was dark and we were ready, we stood with Aunty Vera at our lane end to wait for the Hull bus. Me and Gwendy had our macs on "In case it rains," Mam said, so we didn't look as if we were going to anywhere special but we certainly were and that was all that mattered for now. We were not thinking about what we looked like anymore because we were so excited.

When we got to the clay road that led to the fair we found out that Mam had been right it was a mess and even though they had put cinders down to dry the mud up it hadn't worked.

We were glad of our serviceable school shoes after all as we hurried along with hundreds of other people in the dark, concentrating on the lights shining on the horizon and listening to songs blaring out and beckoning us to hurry up and join in the fun.

On both sides of the track there were caravans. You could see men in fancy waistcoats and women in flowing long bright dresses putting their make-up on. I peered into one of the caravans. I just couldn't help it. I thrilled to the bright warm lights inside and the excitement pouring out through the open door. I watched a lady in a tight little bathing costume and high-heeled shoes. She was brushing her daughter's brown curly hair and they were laughing together. Then her daughter stood up with her back to us while her mam tied a velvet bow round her long red dress. And then she turned round and I could see her face as she smiled at her mother and I gulped in surprise. It was Melanie and that beautiful lady was Miss Pratt. So, they hadn't gone to Scotland after all, they were here at Hull Fair.

Melanie didn't see me and I didn't want her to because I suddenly did care about what I looked like in my serviceable shoes and crumpled mac. I looked so safe and Melanie looked so exciting. She had escaped to a different world, she wouldn't be stuck with us kids or Ringam School ever again and she would be able to go all over the country with the travelling fair. I expect that she wouldn't have to go to any other school much either because by the time the Kid Catcher caught up with her they would have moved on to another city. Then, just as I walked away to join Aunty Vera and the others, I saw a handsome man in a tight red suit and black cloak and he gave Miss Pratt a big kiss. Then the three of them went off arm in arm towards the bright sparkling lights and the loud music at the fair and I lost sight of them as we rushed on to see the side shows in big, bright sheds.

Inside one there was 'The Littlest Woman in the World' standing near her little house in her little garden with a little fence all round. She was looking out at us through her fence. Her body was tiny but her head was big and she had teeth missing like Aunty Dilly. We gawped at her and edged round her fence and went out again and left her. But before we went I noticed that faraway look in her eyes and I knew that she didn't want to be there. She would just have to sit there, day after day and let everybody stare at her and there would be no excitement in her life. I supposed that she had no choice – but that look in her eyes told me that she would never get used to it.

Next, we went to see some fleas in ballet dresses all fluff and frills just like Helen, though much tinier of course. They were doing dances and tightrope walks when their owner shouted at them and cracked his little whip. Then we paid to go and see 'The Greatest Escapologist in the World' and he turned out to be the man in the tight red suit and black cloak that I had seen with Melanie and her mam. In fact, they were all on stage. Fancy me knowing somebody who was on stage.

"I know her," I shouted turning round to the crowd and grinning and pointing to Melanie but nobody answered and nobody cared; they were all too busy holding their breaths as Miss Pratt tied the man up with ropes and chains and put locks on and put him in a bag. Then Melanie turned the key of the final lock. After a few minutes the bag began to move just like the sack with the baby foxes had done. It was a little movement at first and then it got bigger and bigger and more and more jerky until the bag was moving all over the stage while Melanie and Miss Pratt smiled and waved at the crowd to distract us. Then suddenly, just when I wasn't looking at the bag, the man was free and he jumped up with his arms in the air and his cloak flapped behind him. We clapped and cheered and people threw pennies onto their stage. All three of them bowed and curtseyed and then ran off laughing, back down the clay road to their caravan not caring at all about mud getting on their best shoes.

We laughed, as well, when we knocked coconuts down, threw ping-pong balls in goldfish bowls and spiked cards with darts. Terry was brilliant at it all and won two goldfish and we carried them about in their glass bowl, with string round it, spilling water that ran out everywhere.

Aunty Vera saw to it that our money never ran out though. She dipped into her big purse with a laugh as often as we needed so we could go on every ride we wanted and we went shrieking round and round and up and down till we were giddy.

But time ran out and we had to catch the last bus home and even Aunty Vera couldn't change that. We trooped back down the clay road towards a dark horizon and away from bight exciting lights and music.

We got onto a crowded bus back to Gum with our gasping goldfishes with no water. They died before we got home and we chucked them out at our lane end when we got off the bus. We were left with an empty bowl and everybody laughed and I did as well but I wish I hadn't because I felt sorry for the goldfish. I bet they never got used to being in a bowl instead of swimming free in open water and now they were dead.

My dad was not at home when we got back to our house, of course. I knew he was in Scotland but it was very strange and our house felt very empty without him. I wished that he was back at home but it was another two days before our car puffed into our yard and we all crowded round, suddenly shy of these two adventurers. My dad looked thinner and I knew then that it was because he had not been able to get used to the food in Scotland, I never thought that he would.

"It's all mountains covered in heather," said Uncle Sid. "And there's men in kilts. And they played bagpipes when we went into the hotel."

Dad didn't say anything and just came in to our house and sat down near the fire and Mam got him a mug of tea and a big piece of her apple pie. He ate it hungrily. He put a crumpled carrier bag on our table with presents for us all. Our Katy had a silk hanky ('Say handkerchief," said Mam) it had 'Frae Bonny Scotland' embroidered on it. Our Gwendy had a silver heather brooch and I had a tiny metal Scottish dancer wearing a kilt and playing bagpipes. I put some cotton on it and tied it to my charm bracelet next to Scottie dog. I thought they could keep each other company what with them both coming from Scotland. We were all pleased with our presents. Mam was last and she smiled a beautiful smile and took her present in its brown paper bag and peeped inside. And that's when everything changed.

Mam's face went white and her lips went tight and she didn't even put her hand in the bag she just slammed it down on our table. Dad didn't ask what the matter was. He just went upstairs and got into his working clothes and went out to see his animals. Mam shoved the paper bag angrily to the back of our table drawer with tears in her eyes. A bit later that day when she was outside working I had a look in that bag to see what sad thing he had bought. I pulled out a peeler and an apple corer with wooden handles and shiny blades. I couldn't understand what was so bad about them. They would be a big help when she baked her apple pies. But she didn't want them, that much was clear and that night I heard her talking to Dad.

"There's more to life than Gum and work, you know." I didn't hear what Dad said to her but I knew he would say, "You'll get used to it." But I didn't think that she would because nowadays she looked so sad.

No more was said but I noticed that when Mam was rolling her pastry next time she banged the rolling pin down on her board just that little bit harder than she had ever done before. I often saw that faraway look in her eyes now, and she never did use that peeler and corer and soon that shiny steel went rusty and wooden handles went mouldy. Then one day Mam chucked them away. But long before that our new sheep arrived in a big lorry from Scotland.

We all stood round while the lorry rolled into our stack yard. The big back doors were pulled down to make a ramp and we could see the little black sheep with a wild look in their eyes. I expect they didn't like flat Gum very much after their mountains in Scotland. But Dad had got a nice sheep pen ready with fences all around.

"Ci-boy, ci-boy," we shouted which we all knew is sheep language for 'come on' but they were from Scotland of course and didn't understand sheep English so they just stood there and would not come out. The drover had to get in his lorry and grab their woollen backs and push them out one by one. Dad's pen was in our paddock and his idea was that it would help them settle in before they went into a bigger field. But they didn't like our farm or being stuck in their pen one bit. They pushed and rammed at the fence and jumped wildly.

"They'll get used to it," said Dad. "Just give them time."

But they kept on breaking our fences down and when Dad put them in Hoss Paster field they just pushed through hedges and kept breaking out. Dad had to keep putting new bits of fence in to repair the hedges. They never did get used to being at Gum. Those sheep wanted to be free to roam their mountains in Scotland but of course they didn't have that choice. They had to stay at Gum forever trying to break out, which they often did and they were a real nuisance, so Dad and Uncle Sid never went to Scotland for cheap sheep again.

We heard about Melanie and her mam just once more. Uncle Sid read it out of the *Hull Daily Mail* while we were having tea one day. "Local woman marries Fairground Escapologist." It was only a few lines in very little print but my mam smiled a beautiful smile because she was pleased that Miss Pratt was not shameful any more. And I was pleased because it was nice to see Mam smile. She did not smile much these days.

Then one day Mam announced, "I'd like to go away for a bit of excitement, I don't always want to be stuck in Gum." Dad didn't answer and I knew that he wouldn't understand and he just carried on eating his apple pie. He would think, like he always did, that Mam would get used to it and I got a bit frightened in case she ran off like Melanie and her mam.

My mam didn't run off though and nothing more was said. But the next time Aunty Cecily came from London to see Aunty Peggy, Mam packed a bag and went back with her for a holiday down south. When she came home she was all smiles and full of stories of exciting things she had seen. And she had been in posh cafes where people went who had gone up in the world and she told us how they drank out of little cups and ate little slices of sponge cake.

Then next time it was baking day Mam made a sponge cake instead of apple pie because that's what they ate in London.

"I don't like this cake," said Dad with a mouth full of dry sponge. "I'd rather have your apple pie."

"You'll get used to it," said Mam and she smiled at him with her beautiful smile. But he never did get used to eating sponge cake instead of apple pie. I never thought that he would.

Chapter 13

Clouds

When Hull Fair was over, the next thing that we looked forward to was bonfire night. I was so excited and could hardly wait. We always had a big fire and every year we had so much fun and I wanted this year to be even better. But one thing was worrying me and it was that for the last few days there had been big black clouds in the sky and it just did not stop raining. I really hoped that it didn't rain on the actual night. I just couldn't bear it if it rained on bonfire night and then our fire would not light. Everything would be spoilt and this year would not be the best.

"Every cloud has a silver lining," said my dad as he rushed in for his mug of tea before getting on with feeding his animals. I was still worried about rain though. And in any case, last time he had a saying he was wrong, because he said that our sheep from Scotland would get used to living at Gum and they never did. They never stopped trying to break out of their Hoss Paster field. They never did like living at Gum and they would like us even less on bonfire night because our fire was being built in their field. It would frighten them even more than they were already by being away from their home in Scotland. Anyway, over the next few days I just couldn't get it out of my head that maybe our fire wouldn't burn because it was wet. It had not stopped raining yet and maybe it never would, judging by the thick black clouds still in the sky.

To keep us from getting too worried about the rain, us kids tried our best to collect leaves from our wood. We bagged them up and dried them off in our shed. With sacks of dry leaves, we hoped that our bonfire might still burn even if it was raining. Meanwhile, Uncle Sid was cutting our field hedges day after day to build up our bonfire.

It's not a boy!

Mouse always helped Uncle Sid, he was one of our farm workers and of course he was not really called Mouse; that was not his real name. His real name was Michael but we shortened it to Mickey and then because he was such a quiet worker we called him Mickey Mouse. He didn't seem to mind and he just got on with his work with a kind, lopsided grin on his face raking cuttings from hedges and piling them up on our bonfire with his pitchfork. Mouse was a good worker and worked on our farm all the daylight hours and sometimes he stayed on with us to work even when it was dark. You see, Mouse did not have a real home to go to. He lived in Gum Bin.

When you told anybody round here that you lived at Gum they always laughed. Even when you gave it its full name – Gumbalding – they still laughed. You might think that they were laughing at a funny place name but they were not because, if you thought about it, Sunkstead was just as funny and nobody laughed at that. But the thing that made everybody laugh about Gum was that there was a Loony Bin in a big rambling house behind some trees at Gum. Mam said we had to say Lunatic Asylum, but whatever you said people still laughed. They thought that anybody who came from Gum was from The Bin and wouldn't be very good at things and so it was funny. It wasn't fair because as you know I came from Gum and I had quite a few things on my 'What I am good at' list and I was trying to get more things on it all the time. Mouse was good at things as well and it was not just farm work that he was good at. I could tell that he was good at other things because I talked to him quite a lot.

He told me some interesting things – and he read the *Hull Daily Mail* every day. He told me all about sport and he was very interested in football and the games that were played all over the country. Nobody I knew could talk about sport like he could, even Uncle Sid. But even though Mouse was well-read, he still lived in Gum Bin because he hadn't got anywhere else to go.

Dad said that he got put in The Bin for being wild when he was a very young lad. He was accused of stealing and things like that. His parents could not control him and he was too young to go to prison and so he had to go to Gum Bin. As he grew older he settled down but his mam and dad had died so he had to stay where he was.

He came to work for us every day on a Bin Bus that chugged its way on our main road and dropped him off at our lane end. Then at night the bus came back and picked him up again. Mouse was a good, quiet worker and deserved more, my dad said. Sometimes Mouse even stayed working long after his bus had gone and he had to walk back to The Bin. But Mam said that he couldn't better himself and get on in the world however hard he worked because he was from The Bin and nobody would give him a good job to earn good money. He wore torn and very old clothes with his trousers tucked into his wellies and his hair stuck up like straw. He had to do manual labour all day long every day without any hope of anything different. But he seemed to like working on our farm and especially making our bonfire really big.

Uncle Sid was still cutting more and more branches from trees and clippings from our hedges and every day Mouse was helping him. He was piling them up in Hoss Paster just above where our Big Billy was buried and just next to our railway line where trains rattled past with a whistle on their way from Hull to Ripsea.

Of course, our little Scottish sheep were still trying to get out. Mouse talked gently to them and tried to quieten them but they stamped and stared at him with their wild eyes. They were stuck here with us whether they liked it or not and so was Mouse. But unlike our little sheep, Mouse never gave us any idea that he would like to be anywhere else – he just kept helping us with our bonfire. He even helped us make our Guy Fawkes.

We made our Guy out of two sacks that we stuffed with leaves just like Mam had done to make my mattresses except she used straw not leaves. One big sack was his body and one little sack was his head. Dad's old sports jacket and a pair of worn-out trousers of Uncle Sid's fitted him a treat. We gave him some straw for his hair, and stuffed some old holey wellies on his feet and tucked his old trousers in. Then I painted a grin on his sack face, it turned out to be a lopsided grin so he looked a bit like Mouse – only better dressed. Our Guy was ready but bonfire night had still not arrived – and it was still raining. And we were still waiting and getting more and more impatient.

Then, when we were fed up of waiting one night, all us kids started to get wild with excitement even though the dark clouds hadn't stopped pouring from the sky. We ran out into the night and tore around faster and faster with our hair glistening and our wet clothes stuck to our bodies. We ran crazily thinking of all the fun of bonfire night and wishing it was bonfire night now. We opened our mouths and stuck our tongues out at the raindrops daring them to spoil our fire on the big night.

"You lot are crackers enough you don't need any crackers for bonfire night," teased Aunty Vera, with a laugh when she saw what we were doing. (Mam said we should call them firecrackers but we called them just crackers for short.) Anyway, whatever you called them it reminded us that you couldn't have bonfire night without them – it just wouldn't be right. So, that night we turned our attention to nagging Dad to get us some and the next day he came back from Ringam with a box of crackers coasting half a crown and a packet of sparklers for us three girls to share.

We all sat round our table and our Katy tipped them out. We had two sparklers each then we took it in turns to choose the rest. None of us wanted the Catherine Wheel (there was always one in the box) because we didn't know what to do with it and so we usually just chucked it on the fire where it was eaten up by the flames. We set about choosing. Our Katy chose hers first because she was the oldest, then our Gwendy then me.

Round the table we went choosing – Katy, Gwendy and then me – soon we had all got five each and there were three left. I was last to choose of course and guess what? I had that last cracker – that useless Catherine Wheel. I just knew that would happen. Anyway, as I was last, I bagged the empty cardboard box to keep my crackers in. I ran off and squeezed it in-between my mattresses next to my charm bracelet.

Then that night when I was in bed I pulled the box out again. I felt every cracker and although it was dark I knew – 'light the blue touch paper and stand clear' – was written on every one. Then I thought about what would happen next when all coloured sparks would go up and there would be a fizzing noise or loud pops and bangs and we would all watch as they climbed into a dark sky and then fell invisibly and silently back down to the ground.

I put my crackers back in their box and stuffed it in between my mattresses again. I could feel some gritty gunpowder that had come out and I rubbed it up and down on my skin and I could smell its explosive dark smell like Dad's gun cartridges. Excitement surrounded me and filled my bed but then a little worry like the clouds in the sky crept up on me to add to the worry of the rain.

This worry was that sometimes your crackers were duds and I was really hoping and hoping that I didn't have any. You see, sometimes when you lit the blue touch paper and stood clear, a cracker didn't take off at all and we waited and waited for the sparks and noises but nothing happened. And that was always a sad thing to happen to your crackers and the worry stayed with me and it would not go away, just like the rain.

I sometimes wondered if Mouse ever worried, he had every reason to, what with that big cloud over his life because he lived in Gum Bin. I wondered if he ever thought that he was a dud and could never take off and get on in the world. Maybe he worked so hard so that he could stop thinking about the cloud hanging over him. And now he was staying even later every night to help me because I was trying to fill more sacks with leaves to go on our bonfire. Terry and our Gwendy had filled loads more than me. To tell the truth I was very glad of Mouse's help because I hadn't been feeling very well since Hull Fair and after running about in the rain and getting soaked I was feeling even worse. I didn't say anything to anybody of course. I didn't want Mam telling me that I couldn't stay out on the big night. I couldn't bear the thought that I might miss all the fun and the best bonfire ever. I had been waiting for it and looking forward to it for so long.

Then at last the great day arrived, our waiting was over. But wouldn't you know? I felt even more poorly. I wondered if it was to do with my poisoning. If it was, then all my plans would be no good and I didn't just mean about bonfire night. You see, it wouldn't be much use having a 'What I am good at' list if I was poorly. The whole idea was that I could better myself so that Mam and Dad would not mind having a girl instead of the boy that they really wanted. They would be proud of me at last if I got on in the world but if I was poorly I couldn't do anything. I wouldn't be any good at all. I would be just like Mouse and stuck all my life.

I had to keep going and hoping that I would soon feel better, that was the only thing I could do. And it worked – I forgot about myself when everybody started getting ready. Terry from next door came rushing in to our house to show us his box of bangers and Stewy brought his very own little selection box. Not long to go now, I thought, but it was still raining.

The sun must have set – not that I had seen it for a few weeks but it was getting dark and everything was happening quickly now. Dad revved up our van loaded with our sacks of leaves in the back with our Guy sitting on top. Then he took off down our lane to Hoss Paster spraying water from the road on us kids who were all running and screaming behind. I skidded and my knees buckled a bit but I ran on through darkness following everybody else down to Hoss Paster.

I watched with my heart racing as Dad chucked our Guy with our sacks onto the bonfire. Then Mouse got some matches out of his pocket and tried to light the fire under our leaves but it was no use because it was still pouring with rain, our fire would not burn. This is what I had been so worried about and now everything would be spoilt. But Uncle Sid had another idea.

"Stand back," he shouted as he sprayed a can of petrol on our bags of leaves and then there was an almighty whoosh and gold flames sparkled up into the air. Our fire leapt up into the night. It was only then that the clouds finally gave in and broke up letting the silver moon show through to light up all our faces. A black invisible train rattled past with its whistle blaring. Its yellow lamp faced people were being dragged through darkness and they stared out at us and we waved at them with our arms outstretched. Our little Scottish sheep bleated and stamped as they huddled into a corner of the field never missing a chance to show that they didn't want to be there with us. Then Terry crept round the back of us all and lit his bangers so that we screamed with excitement when they went off with an unexpected explosion. I smelt the smoke in my nostrils from the damp sizzling branches. Then we lit our sparklers and waved them round and round making circles of bright spitting light. The rain clouds hadn't spoilt our fire. The fun had started at last, I thought.

But I was wrong, not about the rain but about the fun. You see, suddenly everything went black for me and everything disappeared and I couldn't see anything. It was as if I wasn't there. There were no faces, no moon, no bonfire – nothing. I huddled my cracker box close to me and began to tremble and then even stranger things started to happen.

Big Billy – dead for years – seemed to roar and heave from his grave below me and the ground underneath my feet began to rock and there was sparkling in my head and banging in my skull. Then I heard a thud.

"She's fallen over," my mam's worried voice floated in from far away. I could feel I was being lifted and I knew I was in my dad's arms because I could smell his pipe and feel his jacket, rough on my face. I heard our van engine start and I was rattled back up our lane to our house held between Mam's soft bust and her strong knees just like when I was a baby.

I was put to bed and there I lay on my straw mattresses too weak even to get my little charm bracelet to bring me luck and keep me safe. The next day everybody crept quietly about because I couldn't stand the slightest noise. If I heard anything it was as if Terry's bangers were going off again in my head and if I saw anything it was sparklers going round and round in front of my eyes. Days went by and I didn't get any better and so our doctor was sent for. Doctor Moon from Ringam was coming to see me and there was a lot of work to be done before he arrived.

First Dad came and picked me up from my own bed and carried me to Mam and Dad's bed. And Mam's best red and gold cover was pulled over me. The old bed springs sagged even under my light weight, it was a big change from my hard, straw mattresses. But I hardly noticed, all I wanted was peace and quiet.

But there was no peace and quiet now; not only because of the bangs and sparkles going off in my head, but because the doctor was coming. He'd been before of course but not to our bedroom and so it had to be made ready for such an important visitor. I heard Mam's sewing machine downstairs as it rattled out new pillowcases and two new curtains with material from Winsea remnant shop — gold and red to match our best bedspread. The half-moon bedside rugs were shaken and dust was dragged out from every nook and cranny. Our furniture was polished till it shone and our bath scrubbed clean of all its scum. All I wanted was peace and quiet but Mam's sewing machine was rattling again until out came a new red and gold nighty for me to wear for my important visitor. At last, it was over and we were ready for Doctor Moon's arrival. I lay exhausted even though I hadn't done anything except lie there trying to bear all the noise.

Then suddenly there he was, sweeping in through Mam and Dad's bedroom door. Doctor Moon's bald head shone as bright as our clean bath and his big white face was looking down at me from way above. My fevered mind thought that it was the real moon staring down on me and I was standing near our bonfire again.

"I will send a blood sample away," boomed Doctor Moon and then he was gone. He didn't glance sideways at our best bedroom all spick and span in his honour. My new nighty that matched the curtains and Mam's best bedspread and our clean bath went unnoticed by him as he swept out. I lay back on my pillow and waited again. After a few days, my results came through and I had got pneumonia. It wasn't my poisoning after all. At least that was a relief.

"You are going to have the new Wonder Drug," said Doctor Moon. "I should say that you are a very lucky young girl because now we have this new drug to make you well again." All I could think was that I hoped it was better than that drug which was supposed to cure teething pain but had poisoned me instead. I hadn't been lucky that time.

This drug, though, lived up to its name and it was different and it really did work so I did gradually get better. I was going to be strong again I was lucky this time and now because Doctor Moon didn't need to come any more, my days in Mam and Dad's saggy bed were coming to an end. I expected to be back on my straw mattresses again any time soon.

My dad had been sleeping in my bed on his own while I was poorly. He had to have his sleep because he needed to work on our farm and he had to have all the energy he could for our livelihood. He couldn't afford to be disturbed by my fevered tossing and turning at night. So, while he slept on his own in my bed, I had got his place next to Mam and she could look after me if I needed it. But something disastrous had happened and the return to my own bed had to be delayed.

My poor old mattresses had collapsed under Dad's weight and straw had burst out all over and my bed wasn't fit to sleep on now. Of course, I had to have a new mattress and it wasn't long before Mam went off on the bus to the salerooms in Hull and bid for a second-hand flock mattress. She got it at a bargain price and Dad rattled off in our van to pick it up. My new mattress was scrubbed down and dried outside in the late, pale sunshine which had come out at last. Mouse lifted my old mattresses downstairs and took them to our stack yard where they could wait for next year's bonfire. Mam swept the old loose straw away and then carried me back to my own bed at last, but I couldn't rest and it was nothing to do with my new mattress or pneumonia.

I couldn't find my bracelet. My little charm bracelet was missing. As you know it had been tucked away in that crack between my two straw mattresses and now it was lost. Of course, there was no crack in this flock mattress and nowhere to hide my treasures. My charm bracelet could not be found. I thought sadly of Helen's little ballet dancer looking at a beautiful bridesmaid rose as she swung on her chain, and my Scottish dancer with my little Scottie dog from Scarborough for company. It was hard to think about them. And my brown wren farthing from Aunty Dilly was gone as well – they were all lost and they couldn't keep me safe and bring me good luck now.

Well, at least somebody I knew had some luck. It was Mouse or I should say Michael because he'd gone up in the world and bettered himself because he had won The Pools. Now I knew why he studied football results so closely. It was because every week he was going in for a competition about them and now he had won. My dad said that he must have been even richer than our important Doctor Moon and Uncle Sid called him Millionaire Michael now that he had all that money. We were pleased for him and the first thing he did was buy a house in Ringam. It was in Millionaire's Row next to Doctor Moon. He left Gum Bin and he left our farm as well which we were not so pleased about because we missed him and he had been a good worker. But he had no need to work now he could live off his winnings.

Then one beautiful day in summer when there was not a cloud in the sky Millionaire Michael came to see us and he was a very respectable man. His big black car rolled into our yard with its sweet humming engine and we all crowded round. Then we stared because sitting next to him in Michael's car was his very own Minnie Mouse. Our Mickey Mouse had got a lovely wife. He had got everything he could ever want. They walked along to our house and we all followed – a long line of us kids and then our mams and dads and then Grandma. I knew that Mam would have scrubbed our house like she had done for Doctor Moon, she would have made some more curtains if she had known we were having another important visitor, but this was a surprise visit so she had not had time to prepare.

We had to show our respect in some way so Millionaire Michael was allowed to sit in Dad's chair near the fire and his wife sat in Mam's chair and that was a real honour. We stood staring while Mam made us all a mug of tea.

Michael looked very different now with his hair slicked back and his shoes of polished shiny leather and his suit that was black with posh hand-stitching. But he didn't look as happy as you would have thought that he would, now that he had all that money and gone up in the world with a wife and all. But then my mind was taken off him because he put his hand in his pocket and brought out my charm bracelet. Oh, my lovely bracelet! I dashed to get it back.

"I reckon it was this that brought me luck with The Pools," he said quietly. "I found it among straw from that old mattress and guessed it was yours but in all the excitement I forgot about it till now." He held it out to me. You see, Michael was not a thief whatever anybody had said about him in his younger days. I was so glad to see my bracelet and I put it on my wrist straight away to keep it safe. I couldn't believe I had got it back at last and judging by the jangle my charms made, they were happy to be back as well.

Michael still did not look happy though and he didn't look as if the cloud over his life had gone. My clouds had gone now and I wished that his had as well. Everything was sorted for me and even though I hadn't had a good bonfire night at least I could look forward to next year. I'd got my lucky bracelet back and I still had my 'What I am good at' list to get on with. But Michael hadn't got what he wanted. You see, being rich was not as good as Michael had thought it would be, because he didn't know anybody in Millionaire's Row. Also, he had always been used to working and he said that he just didn't know what to do with himself all day long in that big posh house which didn't feel like a real home to him.

Then I had a good idea and I went under-stairs and got my old box of crackers. On bonfire night, I had been so poorly that I hadn't been able to light a single cracker from my box. I had dropped it on the wet ground when I fell and everything had spilled out but our Gwendy had gathered my crackers up and brought them back for me. My grubby squashed cardboard box with its precious contents had been left on a shelf all this time under-stairs. Everybody had forgotten about them but I had not. My idea was that we could light them now and it would cheer Michael up.

We all went outside and Michael got his new gold lighter out and then he lit 'the blue touch paper' on each of my crackers in turn and we stood clear to wait and watch but, believe it or not, they were all duds. I was so disappointed as we waited and waited and nothing happened.

I suppose they got wet when I dropped them and the powder would have all stuck together and they were no good now. All I had left was my boring old Catherine Wheel and I didn't know what to do with it, but Michael had an idea. He took it and pushed one of Mam's pins through it and fastened it to our wooden gate post. Then he lit it with his gold lighter and to our surprise it fired up and went round and round for ages and ages, fizzing with sparks flying everywhere. Then we all laughed and Michael grinned his old lopsided grin and ran his hands through his smoothed hair so it stuck out like it used to do.

Not long after that Michael sold his new house at Ringam and moved with his lovely wife to a little cottage in Gum. You see, he didn't think Gum was a place to laugh about because that's where his friends were. He had a real home now and he smiled his lopsided smile even stronger every day. He didn't come back to work on our farm though – he went to do voluntary work at Gum Bin, where he had lived for so long. He did gardening and odd jobs with his friends who still lived there. He had gone back to looking scruffy and you wouldn't have known that he was a millionaire but if you looked at his even bigger lopsided smile you might have guessed that his cloud had a silver lining at last.

It's not a boy!

Chapter 14

The Lord Mayor

When I went back to school after being poorly I had missed a lot of work and it was hard for me to catch up. I was getting worried about my 'What I am good at' list because I hadn't been able to work on it. It was just before Christmas and things had not been going well what with being in bed and being poorly for so long. It was a bit of a low time for me at the end of that year. If I wasn't careful all my plans to get on in the world would be wasted and I would be going down instead of up.

At school, I knew that I had gone from the bottom to about somewhere in the middle of the class with my work. Brenda and me were the same — we weren't high up at the top but we weren't low down at the bottom either. We were just 'happy medium' and I was trying really hard to keep on going up but having pneumonia had stopped my plans for a few weeks.

Charley was still at the bottom of our class of course because he wasn't bothered about anything but there was another lad down there and he was bothered about it. He was unhappy because nobody liked him much and because he was so fat we all called him Fatty. I didn't tell my mam that we called him Fatty because she would just say we had to call him plump but Plumpy just didn't sound right so I kept quiet.

Fatty was so fat that he couldn't get into ordinary boys' trousers and he had to wear his dad's big trousers with cut down legs. And his waist band was under his arm pits and held up by tight braces that buttoned onto his trousers. He couldn't play with the other lads in our playground because he couldn't run very well what with being so fat and anyway nobody wanted him. Everybody teased him and laughed at him and he so much wanted to join in with everybody's games but the more he

161

wanted to join in the more we laughed at him. Then he went and told our teacher and we all got into trouble and we all hated Fatty even more.

We had another lad that nobody played with as well but he was different. He was called Edmund and he was very high up in our class. Well he was at the top really. You see, Edmund Wright was very rich because his parents had a big farm and his dad was a gentleman farmer. Edmund's dad had inherited money and so he was a very important man. Mr Wright was very fat like Fatty but nobody thought this was funny or anything and my mam didn't even say he was plump she said that he was well-built. I thought he was well-built but fat-rich.

Edmund always looked rich because he was the only child who wore suits to school and his posh short trousers always matched his jacket. He always wore a white shirt and tie as well, not at all like our other lads who wore ordinary trousers with jumpers knitted by their mams.

We mostly left Edmund alone and took no notice of him but he was different from Fatty because he didn't seem to mind. He just sat there at his own desk getting on with his work. And when it was playtime he just stood there with his nose in a book till our whistle went. At home time his dad usually picked his son up in his well-built smooth rolling car, but sometimes Edmund came to school and rode home on his posh bike. So, there it was Fatty and Edmund both with no friends but for different reasons – Fatty, because he was so fat and at the bottom of our class and Edmund because he was fat-rich and at the top.

But now I'd got back to school after being poorly I noticed that things had changed and our kids were not leaving Edmund alone like they usually did. You see, they had been practising for our school Christmas concert. We did it every year in Ringam village hall and our mams and dads came and it was a big thing for everybody.

That year our class was doing *Dick Whittington* and all the parts had been given out while I was away. I was very sad that everybody had got their part in the play and there was nothing left for me to do. It didn't seem fair that I wasn't in *Dick Whittington* because I knew that I could easily learn the lines. I had only heard them practise once and I already knew most people's parts off by heart.

Edmund had got a part of course. In fact, he was Dick Whittington and that's why things had changed. Miss McBride had given him THE best part in our Christmas play. Suddenly instead of taking no notice of Edmund, the kids in our class started to not like him and they started to mumble that it was not fair and that he only got the part because his dad was fat rich.

The girls in our class were acting out the parts of posh ladies in London who met Dick, and the lads were the mice — apart from Charley who was going to be Edmund's cat. I was going to be nothing and it bothered me a lot. All that the other kids were bothered about though was that Edmund had been chosen for THE best part and the mumbling got louder. Fatty loved this because he was going to be a mouse with the rest of the lads and he got let off being teased now Edmund was getting all the hate. Fatty even joined in and mumbled about Edmund. It was a way for Fatty to be part of our lads' gang at last; things just got better for him but things got worse and worse for Edmund. As Fatty went up Edmund came down because the lads were all angry that he had got the part of Dick Whittington. Edmund tried not to take any notice and he tried to read his book and ignore us all even more.

Then one day there was big trouble and Edmund had to take notice, in fact we all did. Edmund came to school with a bloody nose and he was dragging his now twisted bike behind him. His mother, Mrs Wright, was marching along by his side and she strode into our classroom dangling Fatty by the scruff of his torn jumper. She was a tall thin lady and she must have been very strong as well because Fatty could hardly walk, she was holding him up so high, he was on his tiptoes and just dangled there. His dad's mucky trousers had got torn and his fly buttons strained over his big belly while his fat legs lost all control and

163

just hung, helpless. We all gawped in terror from our desks as she dragged Fatty up to face us all.

"This thug and his gang strung a wire across the road, deliberately unseating my son from his bicycle and then they left him injured and bleeding in the road," she shouted. We were all stunned into silence. Our teacher, Miss McBride, flinched and then scurried out leaving us all scared and not knowing what Mrs Wright would do to us. But she did nothing except stare at us all and it was only seconds later that Miss McBride came rushing back with Mr Bantam, our Headmaster, in tow. Edmund's Mother did not even glance at them though and she still stared at our class.

"Who are the other evil boys who perpetrated such an act?" She looked over at Edmund who by now was sitting at his desk with his bloody nose pouring into his white hanky and all down his clean shirt and smart grey suit. "I demand to know." Then she dropped Fatty who started to bawl his head off and slaver came out of his mouth and big watery bubbles came out of his nose. He wiped them with his sleeve and left big grey streaks across his cheeks. Mrs Wright carried on staring at us and I licked my lips and went red and felt as guilty as if I was the one that had put the wire across the road, which of course I wasn't. I held my breath. Still nobody answered.

Edmund's mother sat down on our teacher's chair which nobody else was ever allowed to do, but still there was silence. She crossed and un-crossed her long legs and stared at us all and we stared back. She was wearing a smart costume like my mam wore when we were going anywhere posh, like Ireney's wedding.

"I know you bad boys hid in the shrubs after setting a cruel trap for my son. Then you ran away laughing when he was hurt. I insist on you giving yourselves up to be punished." I looked at Mr Bantam with a triangle of skin on his bald head flashing white then red, it did that when he was angry. I looked at Miss McBride standing to attention with her arms by her side, staring straight ahead. I looked at Fatty sobbing on floor. Of course, he had joined in when the rest of our lads were doing this trick to be part of their gang but when they darted away he wouldn't have been able to because he was so fat he couldn't run very fast – well he couldn't run at all really. So, he got caught by Edmund's Mother while everybody else escaped.

"I'm waiting," shouted Mrs Wright. Nobody said anything and nobody moved. I still held my breath.

"I have plenty of time," she re-crossed her legs again. I looked over to Edmund, blood was still pouring out and I didn't think he had plenty of time because his face was as white as a sheet. Then he keeled over just like I did when I got pneumonia. He fell off his seat and crumpled onto the floor near his desk. Our fearful eyes jerked to him then back to his mother who now got up and marched over, picked him up and carried him out.

"I have to look after my child now, Mr Bantam," she shouted over her shoulder. "But I trust that you will identify the culprits and penalise them by withdrawal of privileges, and corporal punishment." The door slammed into the terrifying silence behind her. Mr Bantam was very red and his triangle on his bald patch was flashing faster so I could tell he was really angry as he took Fatty off for 'an interview' in his office. I breathed out at last.

Well of course Fatty told – we all knew he would. He gave names of lads who had done it and whose idea it had been (Charley's) even though he must have known that they would not let him back into their gang ever again.

But nobody was thinking about that now, they were thinking about what would happen to them. Everybody who had been in on that trick on Edmund was caned and of course that included Charley because he had been their ringleader. They went in to be caned one by one to Mr Bantam's office and they all came out saying that it didn't hurt even though you could see some of them were very red and some of them were very white and all of them looked a bit shaken. But they just shrugged and said that they didn't care.

Charley lost his part in our play because he was the ringleader so he had his privileges withdrawn like Mrs Wright said. But everybody else was allowed to stay in our *Dick Whittington* play because they were the mice and we just didn't have any other kids left to take their parts. But how could we manage without a cat? We couldn't do Dick Whittington without a cat, so nobody knew what was going to happen.

Well you might have guessed – I was given Charley's part – I was in our *Dick Whittington* at last, and Charley said that he didn't care and he didn't want to be in our silly old play anyway so that was alright.

But it wasn't really alright because for one thing I knew I had only been given the part because I was the only one left to do it and for another I didn't have much to say in the play. In fact, there was only one line for me to say and I could have learnt hundreds of lines. Mostly, all I had to do was 'meow' and act like a cat which was easy because we had loads of them on our farm and so I easily knew what to do. This didn't seem to be a good way to get things on my 'What I am good at' list and go up in the world but there was nothing I could do about it and at least I had a part now.

On our concert night, we all met back stage at Ringam village hall, we were so excited. Edmund, now quite recovered, looked really posh even though at first, he was supposed to look poor and down. Of course, for this part at the beginning of the play he could have just worn old holey clothes, but no – he had a special stage costume hired from a theatre in Hull. He had a soft little pair of beige trousers tucked into clean 'gum boots' which is what he called his wellies. There was a pretty red patch neatly sewn over a hole, that wasn't there, on his trousers and a matching red bundle on a stick to go over his shoulder.

My mam made my outfit. She made me a cat suit with tight black trousers and top which she stitched together to make them all in one. She made me a little cat head and mask from Aunty Cecily's astrakhan collar – once her coat wasn't the height of fashion in London she had sent it up north to us in case the fashion reached us one day. Anyway, Mam got fed up of waiting and she cut the collar up and made it into a cat's head and mask for me. Then she made a curly black tail and pinned it on my bum.

When I was ready Dad had rattled me to Ringam in our van – it wasn't our weekend for our car. He dropped me off at the village hall. Then he went rushing off back home to get the milking done with Mam. He wasn't keen on plays and things like that but Mam was, and I knew she would try and get her work done and then come and see us all.

So here I was backstage ready for our play. There were loads of us squashed up there and we were all shouting and laughing and pushing up against each other in our excitement. Then suddenly there was that voice we knew all too well.

"Come along for make-up, everyone," that was Mrs Wright, Edmund's Mother, shouting at us. She had great big sticks of face colours in her hand. "You boys should not be going on stage at all but as Mr Bantam has not seen fit to withdraw that privilege we can't have you going on without make-up, now can we?" Nobody answered – she scared us stiff and nobody wanted her make-up. Then all at once she grabbed one of our lads and daubed his face. She put a great gob of blood red on his nose just like when Edmund's nose was bleeding. Then she scraped on big grey streaky whiskers just like when Fatty wiped his runny nose with his sleeve and left grey streaks. I thanked my lucky stars that my mam had made me a cat head and mask that covered most of my face.

When Mrs Wright had finished, our lads looked stupid (except Edmund, of course) with bright red noses and rough grey whiskers all over their cheeks. At last they hung their heads. Looking stupid hurt them more than any caning that Mr Bantam could do.

Suddenly lights went out and there was silence. Floodlights came on and Mr Bantam, all dressed up in his best suit, white shirt and bow tie pushed his way through a gap in the heavy stage curtains.

It's not a boy!

"Ladies and Gentlemen…" I couldn't see him now of course, because I was standing in the wings with Edmund waiting for our play to start. I wanted it all to go well and I wanted Mam to be proud of me and my class even though I was only a cat. I really hoped she finished milking in time.

Two dads pulled on ropes and the curtains parted. Mr Bantam went to sit in the audience and on strode Edmund with me following behind scurrying on all fours. The lights shone blindingly on us both.

"I am going to London to go up in the world," shouted Edmund his voice was loud and clear, he was really good and he had all the audience looking and listening. I saw his mother just past the lights flooding the stage; she was on the front row with her arms folded and with a proud smile on her face. The dads in the wings pulled some cardboard signposts across the stage while Dick Whittington walked and walked with me still scurrying behind.

When we got to London, Dick was a down and out and had to sleep in an awful room. And when our lads, dressed as mice, ran on stage everybody laughed loudly at them with their bright red noses and rough whiskery lines all over their faces. They must have felt even more stupid but everybody started to like them and some of them started to act about and make the audience laugh even more, but this time it was a nice laugh.

As you know, Dick decided to leave London because he found that it was harder than he thought to go up in the world (I could have told him that) and our backstage dads rang some bells and we all shouted out:

"Turn again, Whittington. Lord Mayor of London."

"You can do it, you can be Lord Mayor," I said and that was my only line. And then as you also probably know, Dick did turn and he went back and he got rich and famous all because his cat (me) chased every mouse from posh people's houses. And Dick was made the Lord Mayor for saving everybody from mice. Then there was just a last line that he had to say.

'The prophecy of the bells is fulfilled and I am the Lord Mayor of London.' The bells would ring again then everybody would clap and the lads would bow and the girls would curtsey. The curtains would be drawn and that would be the end of that.

But it didn't happen like that because guess what? When we got right to Edmund's last line and we were all waiting. He didn't say anything. Everything went deadly quiet. I was sitting at his feet purring like a cat should and I looked up into his face and it was then that I realised something awful – Edmund, the Great Lord Mayor of London, had forgotten his lines. He went red – he looked out into the wings but nobody was there except the two dads ready to ring bells and then pull the curtains shut. Miss McBride had been so sure that Edmund would not forget his lines that she had gone and sat next to Mr Bantam in the audience. I stopped purring. Mrs Wright began to frown and her smile disappeared.

We waited. 'Come on, Edmund, you can do it,' I thought. But Edmund couldn't do it and his face went from red to white. I held my breath. Of course, I knew what words came next but if I told Edmund his lines I would show him up in front of everybody and his mother would be angry with me and would want me punished. Also, the kids in our class wouldn't be pleased to see me helping Edmund and I might be like Fatty who nobody wanted. But if I didn't do something our play would be spoilt.

This is what I did. I breathed out at last and took another deep breath then I jumped up and put my hands on Edmund's shoulder as I pretended to cat-lick his ears and everybody laughed. It was a gentle laugh though and not one that made me feel stupid or anything like that. Then while they were laughing I secretly whispered, "The prophecy of the bells is fulfilled..." Edmund nodded ever so slightly then he smiled at the audience and shouted his last line.

"The prophecy is of the bells is fulfilled, I am the Lord Mayor of London." And then our backstage dads rang the bells again and everybody clapped and clapped and we bowed and curtsied and then went off stage and the curtains were drawn. I was pleased to see that my mam had got there in time to watch most of our play and we went home together on the bus. She didn't say that I was good as Dick's cat. I bet she was disappointed that I didn't have a better part so she could be more proud of me. I didn't tell her what I had done to help Edmund though, because she might have thought I was jealous of him, so I kept quiet.

Next day at school it was all back to normal. Fatty was trying to join in our games again and be part of our lads' gang but of course he still couldn't run and of course nobody wanted him. Edmund was reading a book and nobody was taking any notice of him.

I did think Edmund would take notice of me though and that he would be very pleased with me and come and thank me for telling him his words when he had forgotten them but he didn't say a thing. So, to cheer myself up, I decided to put – learning off by heart – on my 'What I am good at' list. I was pleased to have something more on it at last.

The next day I was even more pleased because Edmund came running up to me at dinner time. Without saying a word, he pushed a little letter in my hand and rushed off. It was an invitation to his very own Christmas party – he hadn't even put his message in Miss Kenny's basket but had brought it straight to me. I could hardly believe that I would be going to such an important party.

Mam's preparations began straight away. She seemed pleased that I had got that invitation because she said that I needed a new dress. It must have been more important than when I went to Helen King's because then I only wore my school dress. The other thing, that was different now, was that I did not give up my 'What I am good at' list this time – I had learnt my lesson with Helen, and knew that even posh friends may not help you get on in the world, my list would do that.

Mam went off to Ripsea the very next day and bought some pink taffeta and net and then she rattled away on her machine and made me a beautiful dress with the net over it and she embroidered loads of flowers and stitched loads of sequins on it by hand. My hair was put in ringlet rags overnight so little springs hung down all over my head. I even got washed in our bathroom this time and not our steamy wash house. I was allowed some of Mam's proper lipstick as well but only a little bit just to colour my lips. Mam smudged it on with her finger. When I was ready Dad took me in our car. We went to The Ringam Hotel which was just opposite to our grocery shop where we did our Saturday shopping. But there was none of that now I was going to a posh party – thank goodness it was our turn for our car, it wouldn't have looked good if I had rattled up in our van. When we got there, Dad shoved me in through a big front door and then rushed off as fast as he could because he was in a hurry to get back to our cows and in any case, he didn't like parties and that sort of thing.

I edged in and stared round in surprise. There in that big, big room were loads of kids and I didn't know any of them, there was nobody from our class except Edmund of course. He was crowded round by people giving him presents. I was suddenly so scared and I couldn't move forward, I just stood there as if I was frozen to the floor.

Then Edmund saw me and came towards me smiling. "Come on, you can do it," he said kindly and I handed him a present which I wouldn't have minded for myself. Mam had gone to the post office in Ripsea, when she bought my material, and bought a five-shilling postal order for me to give. I had never had so much money myself but I bet it wasn't much to Edmund. Anyway, he did something next which surprised me very much. He leant towards me and put his hand on my shoulders and his mouth to my ear and he whispered, "Thank you, thank you very much indeed." And I knew that he wasn't just thanking me for his postal order. And then do you know what he did? He kissed me – right on my just slightly lip-sticked lips and I felt on the top of the world just like when I had won that painting competition.

We played Postman's Knock and I got another kiss from Edmund. In Blind Man's Buff Edmund guessed me and in Pass

171

the Parcel, even though Edmund won, he let me unwrap a layer of paper twice. His mother smiled at me then and I thought that she was not so bad after all. I never left Edmund's side all night. I wanted it to last for ever but after what seemed like a very short time I saw my mam come though the big door to take me home. I could hardly wait for the next day at school, when I would see my new friend – Edmund – again.

When I spotted him riding to school on a new posh bike I ran up to him but to my surprise he didn't say anything. And at playtime I stood near him – might he kiss me again? But Edmund didn't even speak to me or smile in fact he didn't look up from his book once. So I was back to being happy with Brenda and I didn't mind too much though because the other kids might not have liked me if I was friendly with Edmund. And I've told you that I didn't want to be like Fatty who nobody wanted. I didn't think that Edmund's kisses could have made up for that. I decided to forget about him and after all I had Christmas to look forward to.

I got a new bike on Christmas Day – well it wasn't new, not like Edmund's – it was my old one painted up by Dad, with its brakes tightened and a new bell fastened on. But anyway, it looked quite good. And another thing I got was a game of Snakes and Ladders and Brenda came and we played it all day and sometimes she went up ladders and sometimes I did. And sometimes she came down snakes and sometimes I did as well. It didn't worry me too much when I went down a snake because it was only a game. In real life, I had got something extra on my 'What I am good at' list and I had been to Edmund's posh party and the Lord Mayor had kissed me. Things were looking up for me again at last.

Chapter 15

The Picnic

As you know, Aunty Vera had another baby after she had Terry and Stewy. I didn't know she was going to have one, it was just that one day she went into hospital in Hull and when she came back after about two weeks she had a new born baby. It was a beautiful little girl and her name was Veronica and as she grew up and tried to talk she called herself Beronny because she couldn't say Veronica so we shortened it to Bonny. We always called her Bonny – and it really suited her, she was so sweet and pretty and well, just Bonny. She had pale white skin with rosy cheeks and bright blonde hair that shone as if sunshine was glowing out from it. Here was a perfect little girl for Aunty Vera at last, who was very pleased indeed to have a girl for her third child. A third girl for my mam and dad was not such good news. But Bonny was good news because Aunty Vera and Uncle Sid were not looking for a boy to work on our farm because they already had two. So, we could all welcome Bonny and love her very much.

We carried Bonny everywhere round our farm and played with her all day when we weren't at school. She joined in all our games and she used to come with us into our stack yard when we climbed our bales and made dens. She was always laughing and reaching up with her little chubby arms for a cuddle and when we got home from school we charged off to find her and see who could be first to get a hug.

But one Saturday when Bonny was still a toddler we decided to go for a picnic where our village church was. To get there you had to walk for ages on our main road and then walk up one of our fields called Green Hill. It wasn't really a hill just a little bit of a hump for Gum Church to stand on but it was a hill to us because the rest of our land was so flat.

Aunty Vera didn't want us to take Bonny with us to Green Hill because it was too far away and anyway a little girl would not be able to walk all that way and she would be too heavy for us to carry so far. Bonny was very sad to see us going and big tears welled up in her beautiful eyes.

"We'll bring you some of our picnic back and you can come with us when you're older," I told her as the tears spilled over onto her rosy cheeks.

So, we set off – Terry, Stewy, our Gwendy and me – and we waved cheerio to a crying Bonny who stood on our lane with her arms held out, hoping for one of us to run back and pick her up and give her a hug and carry her with us. I can tell you, it was very hard to turn our back on her but we did and we set off up our lane and on to our main road leaving her behind. I was very sad at first thinking of Bonny's tears but then I forgot all about her because I had been allowed to take my bike and I was so excited.

There was only me that was allowed to take a bike because Dad had put a bell on mine when he had it done up for Christmas and nobody else had one on theirs and you had to have one if you went on our main road. The others' bikes were not roadworthy said Uncle Sid, and he knew about those sorts of things.

We took it in turns to ride but Terry grumbled because it was a girl's bike and had no crossbar and who wanted a silly old bell anyway? When it was your turn, you had to ride to a telegraph pole and then get off and leave the bike on the road side and start to walk so when the next person got there they could ride it to next pole and so on. I rode first because it was my bike and I noticed that when it was Terry's turn he shot off on it at top speed, he rode very well even though it didn't have a crossbar for boys. The rest of us ran along as fast as we could and you could hear our wellies slapping on our legs and our money jangling in our pockets. We were going to Gum village shop to buy our picnic.

I had two pennies that I had saved for so long I couldn't remember where they had come from. I kept them in my old cracker box under my bed with my charm bracelet. They were cold and black and I often held them in my hand till they were warm. They both had Queen Victoria's head on and I liked that because it was my name. One was when she was young and had pretty ribbons flying in her hair and the other one was when she was an old lady with scarves on her head and a serious look on her face as if she was going to die soon.

Terry was our best runner and he was up front, then came our Gwendy and then Stewy and then me. It was a hot day and I was longing for a drink of sarsaparilla, that's what we would get from our shop – fizzy, sour sarsaparilla. Round village corner I went – and puffed up some stone steps where they were all waiting for me in the hot sun. We pushed on the shop door and it creaked open.

'Clang-clang' went a bell as we fell into a pitch-black room with a cold stone floor. It was a grave room with no sunshine. We were boiling hot from running and cycling and glad of the cold room at first but as we stood waiting and waiting we began to freeze and shiver. We could die in here and nobody would know. Staring into the gloom we strained our ears till at last we heard the faint shuffling of Miss Smith's slippers slowly getting nearer until she loomed up from the shadows.

Miss Smith was our shopkeeper and she reminded me of my old Victoria with her head covered in scarves and a serious look on her face. She looked very old as if she was going to die soon.

"A bottle of sarsaparilla, a packet of crisps and some chewy," said Terry ('Say chewing gum,' Mam used to say, but we never did).

"And what else?" said Miss Smith but we hadn't got money for anything else and we all stood very still staring at her and not understanding. Then Terry remembered to be respectful and say

"Pleeease," which was what Miss Smith had wanted all along. We fished our money out of our pockets and spread it out on the cracked wooden counter. I didn't mind spending my old penny but I was quite sad to say goodbye to my young queen with pretty ribbons in her hair.

Now we had our picnic and we took the bottle and packets and burst out through the door glad to be in the sunshine again. We warmed up quickly and we were all longing for a drink. We sat on the shop steps, Terry went first with the sarsaparilla because he got there first and I was last. When it was my turn I grabbed the bottle, and took great gulps. I wiped my mouth and I loved the cold fizzy sour taste going down my belly and bubbles came back up and into my nose. Then we all tried to belch and I couldn't do it very well so I couldn't put it on my 'What I am good at' list yet. Terry was brilliant at it. Great big loud noises came up from his belly and out through his wide-open mouth – we shrieked and laughed and he did it again and again. I was jealous and determined to practise so that I could be better than him.

When we had finished, Terry took our empty bottle to Miss Smith and she gave him some money back and so he bought a quarter of goodies ('Say sweets,' Mam told us) in a bag. Now we were on our way again we left my bike on the roadside grass and set off across our field to Gum Church sitting on Green Hill. We went straight to the churchyard.

We loved walking among hundreds of old graves reading what was written on their headstones. We read them again and again. I looked at my granddad's who died because he was very old. Then I found a lovely little grave, it was so tiny, which was why I had never noticed it before. It was for a little girl and her name 'Isabel' was carved on the headstone entwined with some stone flowers. I was shocked to see that she had died when she was only Bonny's age. I read the inscription over and over again.

'I plucked this tiny flower'
Said the Gardener

'To dwell in my heav'nly bower'

Well, I for one thought that the Gardener had plucked this little flower called Isabel too soon. She should have been allowed to stay and bloom into a beautiful young woman. Instead she had died and to show how sorry I was I picked some wild flowers for her grave. I put some on my old granddad's as well but I saved my best for that little girl because she had been plucked too soon. What a lovely name Isabel was.

"When I grow up I'm going to call my little girl Isabel," I sighed.

"Isabel. Is-a-bell. Is a bell necessary on a bike?" laughed Terry and we all shrieked with laughter. I laughed as well but I wish I hadn't because I felt sorry for little Isabel. Anyway, we all stopped laughing soon because we went into Gum Church where it was very black and cold and not at all funny.

We pushed its big wooden door open a crack and it pushed us back and creaked, not wanting to let us in. We pushed inside and it was just like being in Miss Smith's shop without any sunshine. It was certainly not the sort of place where you laughed.

"You have to pray," said Terry as he sat down and a dark pew swallowed him up.

"What do I say?"

"Shh – you have to be respectful." So, we all sat down. I sat next to Terry and bowed my head to pray but no words came. I didn't know what to say. I only knew one prayer that I had learnt at Sunday school. But somehow, I couldn't even remember a single word of that now – so I just kept my head down and I didn't pray I just whispered, "Pleeease," without knowing why and I squinted out of my eye corner till I saw Terry get up and go out and then I copied. We all tiptoed out and when we felt the sun shining on us we were full of life again and laughed and ran as fast as we could.

It's not a boy!

We ran to our secret island surrounded by a black moat just behind Gum Church. There was an old crumbly brick bridge from the graveyard leading to our island but we never used it. You see, our way was blocked by a little old gate that had been chained shut and locked with a rusty old padlock. If we wanted, we could easily climb over but we never did because that bridge was so ancient and wobbly that if you just set one foot on it you would go down with it into the moat and drown. So, we had found another way to cross.

Our crossing was made from a tree that had grown so old that it had died and fallen – its roots were in our field and its branches fell on our island. All we had to do was walk across its trunk and then we were there. Now it was time to eat our picnic.

We all sat down on some grass and Terry shared out some crisps and they made us thirsty again and so we had to suck on our goodies with hardly any spit left in our mouths while Gwendy told us a story that our Katy had told her about a big house that was once on this island. It stood proud and tall and inside there were all sorts of gorgeous things of gold and silver because the owner was a very rich man. He had chosen this island as a special place for him and his wife to live because it was so beautiful. Then one day his wife had a baby girl and she was good news because they were not farmers and they were not waiting to have a boy. They called her Isabel and they both loved her so much they gave her hundreds of toys and she could have anything she wanted and all her clothes were of fine silk and satin. Then one day something terrible happened – this little girl wandered off on her own and fell in the black moat and she was drowned – and that little girl was buried in Gum churchyard. Her mother and father could not bear to live on their island anymore and they chained the gate up and padlocked it and left, never again to return.

I was sad at first but soon pushed it all to the back of my mind because we had finished our picnic and we were going to play some exciting games.

First, we played cowboys and ran around shooting each other with pretend guns made of rotten branches. When you got shot you had to die. When you were dead you counted to a hundred then you could come alive again and carry on where you left off. When we were fed up of that we played Hide and Seek.

When I was 'It' I counted to a hundred with my eyes closed next to an old hollow walnut tree. It was huge and its bark was rough with deep cracks and crevices – and as I stood there with my eyes tight shut counting automatically. I imagined my little Isabel coming here when this tree was young and maybe her mother picked her some nuts for her to eat – she was a very lucky little girl because I had never even seen a walnut and this tree was too old to have any now. But then of course she wasn't lucky because on one of her trips out when no one was looking she had that terrible accident and drowned and died. My voice trembled and went high and wobbly, "...98, 99,100... coming ready or not."

Off I went searching through overgrown briars and tumbled down trees. I wandered among some old brick rubble that I thought must have been Isabel's house – maybe this was her room where she would have been so happy playing with all her toys but then she got plucked and had to leave it all behind. I kicked some rubble about but there was nothing left of her toys, they had all rotted a long time ago.

I felt very lonely now on my own on that island with memories of dead Isabel. I never liked that part of Hide and Seek when you were on your own and you hadn't found anybody yet.

I wandered about for a long time all alone and I had almost given up trying to find anybody when I suddenly heard a little scuffle just over a pile of bricks, and I crept up and peered over and there was Stewy. I was so glad to see him, I can tell you – he jumped up and we laughed and hugged and held hands as we ran off to find the others.

After ages and ages, we found our Gwendy in a very clever hiding place – she had hidden inside Isabel's walnut tree – it was so old that it was rotten and you could just squeeze inside. Now all we had to do was to search for Terry. But we just could not find him.

"You two go that way and I'll go this way," said Gwendy and so we set off scrambling through brambles and rotten tree trunks till we were all scratched and bleeding but soon we had gone all round our island and met up again and we still had not found Terry. We were tired now and fed up of this game.

"Come out, Terry – you have won," we shouted slumping against the old walnut tree. "We can't find you – come out now." But there was no answer.

"Terry, please come out of hiding – pleeease!" We were getting worried now and desperate. "TERRY!" we yelled but there was no answer just a lapping of black water as a wind got up and made little waves all round us.

We searched again together, shouting but he was nowhere to be found, maybe he had fallen in that deadly moat and drowned like little Isabel. Maybe we would see his body floating any minute now. Frantically I ran to look and sure enough there was something floating by – something black and soaking wet – was it a body? Was it Terry who would never be first again and never do great big belches that made us laugh so much? Well no, now I was nearer I could see that it wasn't Terry it was just a big old log. We kept on frantically searching. Terry, I bargained in my head, if you are safe you can always be the best belcher and I will not try to be better than you at it. Please be safe. Pleeease, I pleaded as we split up to search again.

I was at the old brick bridge now and I held on to its padlocked gate – rusty chains clanked and wouldn't let me through. It was then I saw something even more frightening than the log in the water. There they were in the long grass right at the moat's edge – I stared and stared going hot and cold and hot again – you see, they were Terry's wellingtons, just his wellies standing there on their own without Terry. He must have taken them off to dabble his feet and then he must have fallen in and there was nobody to pull him out.

When I fell in our drain and went down and down – I hit something and then kicked and went up and stretched out my arm and luckily for me a man from that courting couple had seen me and grabbed my hand and pulled me clear. Terry was very strong much stronger than any of us and he would have kicked and kicked fiercely when he hit the bottom, but he couldn't swim – none of us could – and nobody had been there to pull him out.

Gwendy and Stewy rushed over now and we all stood there staring at Terry's wellies. Then we saw a ripple coming to the surface of the water and then a great big loud noise came from below us under the old bridge. The ripple changed into a whirlpool and then like a belch from a belly, Terry exploded from the moat – his hair was streaming over his face and his mouth was wide open to gulp in air. He gulped and gulped and then he pulled on a branch, he dragged himself out and flopped like a drowned Isabel next to us – except that he wasn't drowned. He was full of life.

"Fooled you, I hid in the water," he laughed. "And when I heard you coming I clung onto a branch and held my breath and went under and counted to a hundred, I bet you thought I was dead." We were so pleased that we laughed and laughed even though I didn't think that it was very funny because I had been so scared that Terry had been plucked. Then we all tried to do big belches again but I remembered my promise and didn't try very hard. Terry did the very best one he had ever done and we all shrieked. Belching could never go on my 'What I am good at' list.

We scrambled over our fallen tree trunk and ran off across our field to pick up my bike. Then we set off back down our main road – sharing out our chewing gum as we went. Terry said that he didn't want a go on my bike, he wanted to run about and get his clothes dry. So, us three had more turns riding and it was really good and I rang my bell furiously as I pedalled past him.

It's not a boy!

We were looking forward to getting home to find little Bonny and tell her all about our adventure. It was then I remembered our promise to bring her some of our picnic back and we had forgotten and gone and eaten it all. Never mind we could play with her a bit longer tonight, to make up.

But we didn't play with Bonny that night. You see, we ran into her house next door and she wasn't there, all we saw was Grandma sitting silently – we ran into our house but Bonny wasn't there either. We ran into stack yard where we used to play and she wasn't there either. We didn't find her but we did find a pool of black blood on stack yard floor – a pool of dried blood and big drips of spattered blood.

Mam told us what had happened. You see, Bonny had not gone back into her house after we had set off for our picnic. She must have felt so lonely, like when you play Hide and Seek and you can't find anybody, and so she had gone off into our stack yard by herself to play the games we always played together. She must have climbed our bales and somehow fallen – we never really knew where or how but it must have been from a great height because she was found unconscious by Aunty Vera who had gone to look for her. Bonny's head was gashed open and blood was spurting everywhere. Aunty Vera picked up Bonny's limp body and ran.

"Call an ambulance," she screamed racing into their house to lay Bonny down on their couch and wash her wound. But her wound was huge and couldn't be washed away and Grandma said that they could see Bonny's skull coming through her hair that had gone dark and limp. When she heard the cry for help, Mam raced next door to the telephone and rang for an ambulance.

In no time at all the ambulance came hurtling down our lane. It knew its way from last time when that train had splattered Mr Freddy Lowe.

Bonny was rushed to hospital in Hull and then rushed into theatre – not knowing about anything, not seeing the man who said he was Uncle Sid and not even feeling that awful mask they put on you because, you see, she was already unconscious.

And now we all had to wait and wait and hope and hope and pray and pray. "Pleeease," I whispered again and again. I would easily give up all my 'What I am good at' list if Bonny could come back to us.

But the Gardener was not listening to me, he did not want my 'What I am good at' list. He was already reaching out to pluck Bonny for his 'Heav'nly bower' and she was lifting her arms to be carried away by him. She would be gone like Isabel. I just could not bear it, what if I never saw Bonny again and had to go to her grave in Gum churchyard and see stone flowers instead of her pretty face.

I longed to go and see her in the hospital before it was too late but only Uncle Sid and Aunty Vera were allowed to see her. They were at her bedside talking to her and willing her to come back to us all on earth. And then one day it happened.

Bonny opened her eyes and held out her arms to her mam and dad. She was going to be full of life again. It was weeks before she could come home though, and when she did she had to be carried out of our car by Uncle Sid and there she lay on their couch next to Grandma who sat watching her all-day long. I wasn't allowed to go and see her at first and when I did she looked very tiny but her hair was bright and shining as if sunshine was coming out of it again. And as soon as she saw me she held out her arms which were not chubby now but thin and bony. And then do you know what she said?

"What did you bring me back from your picnic?"

Well that was ages ago but she had remembered what I had promised and of course as you know we hadn't brought her anything, we had forgotten about her and eaten everything all up. She started to cry and so I had a good idea and I ran back to get my charm bracelet and I let her wear it for one whole day and then I promised that we would not go on a picnic again until she was old enough to come with us. Even if it meant carrying her all the way we would never ever leave her behind again and that cheered her up no end.

But we didn't go back to Gum Church for a picnic for a very long time. I didn't want to look at another grave just yet and I didn't want to think about dead people anymore because I kept thinking of how Bonny had nearly been plucked by the Gardener and I just wanted to play with her all day at home, like we always used to.

Chapter 16

To Tell the Truth

My mam and dad always taught us to tell the truth – no matter what had happened you just had to tell the truth and not tell lies. Of course, my mam and dad always told the truth but my dad sometimes used to exaggerate and he said that was different. He said that everybody knew when he was telling a tale and it was just fun. He used to tell a story over and over to different people and as time went on his story changed and got bigger and bigger and better and better.

Do you remember when my dad and Uncle Sid went to Scotland to buy those sheep? Well, they had to stay in a hotel and they hadn't thought about nightwear before they went because at home they used to wear an old shirt or nothing at all if it was warm. And this is the tale my dad told us. "When we got to this very posh hotel a footman comes out and asks for our luggage – well we hadn't got any, we hadn't brought anything with us except the clothes that we stood up in. 'What about your nightwear, sirs?' asks footman. Without another word, we drove off to nearest town and bought a suitcase and some pyjamas and then went back to our hotel and handed our new suitcase, with our pyjamas inside, to the footman."

But next time I heard Dad tell this tale to Aunty Peggy he said, "When we got to this very posh hotel a footman comes out and asks for our luggage and opens our car boot and peers inside. Without another word, we drove off at top speed to the nearest town with our boot lid flapping all the way."

Next time Dad told this tale to Aunty Martha, his footman fell over onto the hotel drive when they hastily drove off with their boot lid flapping and this time they did not bother to buy a suitcase they just bought some pyjamas and handed them in a paper bag to a bemused footman when they got back.

And so his story went on, over time, always changing and always more funny every time it was told. It just got bigger and bigger and better and better. He made us kids laugh and we loved listening to him as he sat near the fire with his mug of tea warming to his tale before he dashed out again to see to his animals. We knew he was only exaggerating to make a good tale and that if you asked him for the truth he was like Mam and he would not tell a lie. If they had a 'What I am good at' list they could certainly have put 'telling the truth' on it, but I could not. You see, once I did tell a lie at Ringam School and even worse, I lied to our Headmaster, Mr Bantam.

This is how it happened. The posh and clever girls like Helen, when she was at our school or a girl in our class called Virginia, used to go up to Mr Bantam at playtime and he used to smile at them and chat to them and then he linked arms with them and they skipped quickly round and round our playground. I really wanted Mr Bantam to do that with me because then everybody would watch me and be jealous and they would think that I had gone up in the world and that I was important. How good I would feel skipping round the playground with him. But even though I was respectful to him, he never even noticed me and never skipped round with me and he never chatted to me or smiled at me, ever.

Then I saw that he noticed you if it was your birthday. When Brenda was ten she ran up to him and told him that it was her birthday and he smiled and said, "Happy Birthday," and chatted to her and he linked arms with her and they skipped round the playground together.

So, I made a plan. One day when Brenda wasn't looking I went up to Mr Bantam.

"It's my birthday today, Mr Bantam," I said – even though it wasn't my birthday for another six months. He looked at me carefully and then he wished me 'Happy Birthday' but he didn't smile and chat and he didn't link up with me and skip round the playground. He did do something else though. He put his hand in his pocket and brought out a sixpence and gave it to me. Then he ruffled my hair with a sigh and walked away before I had even time to say thank you. I looked down at my lovely silver sixpence and I was so thrilled. Mr Bantam had given me sixpence. I kept it in my hand all day long and when I got home I put it in my cracker box under my bed.

It was only when I got into bed that night that I realised what I had done – I had told a lie. It had not been one of Dad's tales it was not an exaggeration for fun it had been an outright lie. I had been given sixpence for telling a lie – and by rights that money should not be mine because I had not told the truth. I couldn't go to sleep but lay there trembling all night.

I daren't tell anyone what I had done. I was very frightened. I daren't even look at my charm bracelet in my cracker box because I would see that sixpence lurking there. It began to cast a big shadow on my life I was so ashamed. So, I made another plan I decided that if I kept busy working with Dad on our farm I might forget what I had done.

On Mondays Dad went to our cattle market in Hull where we sold our animals. This was where we got some money for all Dad and Uncle Sid's work so it was down to the serious business of our livelihood again. One Monday in half-term I went with Dad so I could forget my sixpence. He got changed out of his mucky farm clothes as he always did for market. He put on his sports jacket and his cavalry twill trousers and he even wore a collar and tie. Then he took his best trilby and his cane stick and jumped into our van – I jumped in next to him and we were off. Dad didn't speak at all on our journey – I guess he was concentrating on how much money our beast would make.

When we got to Hull he parked on a roadside just outside market and trotted off in a rush to see how our cattle were getting on and I followed behind him as best I could. Our cattle had gone on before us in a great big lorry that had come into our yard very early that morning. They had been herded inside up a wooden ramp which made them slip and slide and you could see the whites of their eyes because they were frightened. Now they were at the back of Hull market and we found them being checked by The Ministry – they were alright of course but they had even more fear in their eyes. Dad tapped them gently on their bums with his stick and then set off again. I ran after him – we were looking for Ricky.

Ricky was a drover and he was in charge of putting our cattle into a pen. Drovers were easy to spot because they wore long brown coats but they were not always easy to catch because they rushed about from pen to pen.

"How d'ya do?" said Dad to Ricky. My dad liked Ricky and one thing I noticed was that my dad always treated him with respect and tipped his trilby when they met just as if he was as important as my Headmaster. And another thing that Dad did was to give Ricky half a crown. When I asked what it was for my dad just said that it was 'luck money' – a sort of wish that Ricky would bring him good luck in the market.

After we'd had a word with Ricky, we rushed off to Aunty's café. She wasn't really our aunty of course she wasn't anybody's aunty as far as I knew but that's what everybody called her. In we went to a damp, smoky room with rough wooden tables. It was already full of farmers hidden behind great mountains of sausage and mash. It was dinner time.

"How d'ya do?" Dad greeted Aunty and took off his trilby to show respect. Aunty stood behind her big counter. We held out cracked wet plates and big dollops of sausage and mash landed on them. Then we went to a table with farmers that were all dressed like my dad. We all sat round and tucked in. I didn't eat much of it before I was full and then I stared out of the window to the road where our van was parked, waiting to take us home when we had sold our cattle. Dad finished his dinner at last, then he threw a sixpenny tip on the table and with a jolt I was reminded of that one lurking in my cracker box. I jumped up suddenly with the shock of that memory and ran off after Dad to the auction ring.

Dad didn't speak. I knew that he would be thinking hopefully of his cattle and the price they would bring. I was thinking of my lurking sixpence that was mine because I had not told the truth. It had come to the front of my mind again and I tried to push it back. We stood in silence and watched and waited. Sometimes Dad recognised a local farmer or a butcher and he would nod his head and they would nod back. "How d'ya do?"

Then the important auctioneer came and stood on a platform high up above us all. The drovers and people with clipboards were standing about waiting for action. There was a lot of slapping and tapping with a cane and then a bullock was pushed into a barred cage with a floor that moved. He was in a giant weighing scale – a big dial swung above his head and it told you his weight. Then a metal bar was lifted and he was let out into the ring. He charged round and round and his eyes went white with fear and he messed himself and then fell flat in it, then he stood up with his legs splayed out. The drover stood next to him.

"WhatamIbid, whatamIbid," chanted the auctioneer and then bidding started. The auctioneer's head turned backwards and forwards really fast and his hands pointed at us while his fierce eyes probed us for a nod or a touch of a trilby or a pipe taken out of a mouth, which meant you were bidding. I stood frozen to the ground in case I accidentally bought a bullock and I only had a sixpence and I shouldn't even have that and I was still trying not to think about it.

'Bang!' went the auctioneer's hammer but it was not quite over for that bullock. He was slapped out into another cage where his ear had a big hole made in it and he shook his head and red blotches of blood went everywhere.

Then some cattle came in and sales went on all afternoon. My dad didn't move till ours had been sold and they did well and so Dad's luck money must have worked. Then off we trotted and jumped back in our waiting van and went back home.

Dad usually went to market every week and he usually came back pleased because our animals were good and made good money. So, it was a surprise when one day he came back in a quiet mood, I knew something must be wrong.

Then we found out that he was quiet because somebody had crashed into our van when Dad was parked in that road where he always parked. Dad had just jumped in when he heard a loud bang. It was a motorbike that ran into him from behind and there wasn't much damage to our strong van but the motorbike had buckled. Of course, Dad checked that the young driver was alright, which he was. But by the time Dad had got home he was a bit shaken, you could tell. Mam got him a mug of tea and no more was said and weeks went by and we all forgot about it.

Then one day our Posty brought an official letter addressed for the attention of my dad. That was unusual because most farm letters went straight next door to Uncle Sid who always dealt with them because he was good at that sort of thing. Well, this letter was propped up on our mantelpiece when Dad came in for his mug of tea and when he read it he was put off drinking it for quite few minutes which was very unusual so I knew something was wrong again.

You see, that letter was from Dad's insurance company and it was very complicated to read but Mam said that to cut a long story short, the young lad that had crashed into our van was saying that it was Dad's fault and that Dad had backed into his motorbike. Dad said nothing but just rushed out to work again.

That night he sat in his black horsehair chair near our fire and dictated a reply for Mam to write in her best handwriting to his insurance company. She was a neat writer and a good speller and my dad was not good at that sort of thing. When the letter was finished, it said that Dad had only just got in our van and he had not even turned the key to start the engine and so could not under any circumstances have backed into that bike. Dad signed it with a flourish and next morning when Posty came, Mam gave him the letter sealed in an envelope and money for a stamp, then off it went on its way to Hull. She didn't tell our Posty what it was about of course because she didn't want our bad news shouting all over Gum.

"Somebody's not telling the truth, somebody's telling a lie."

It certainly wasn't my dad that was telling a lie, we all knew that and we were glad that the letter had gone back to put the matter straight once and for all.

"That's the end of that," said Dad when he came in for his mug of tea. And we all breathed a sigh of relief and our lives went on as they always had. But we soon found out that it was not 'the end' because one day another letter came from Dad's insurers and it sat on our mantelpiece waiting for his attention. He opened it and his face fell because it said that they advised that a 'compromise' could be reached if they asked for fifty-fifty blame. Knock for knock. Would Dad agree?

Dad would not agree – Dad said he had not even put the key in our van so why should he take part of the blame? After that I got used to brown envelopes going backwards and forwards and Dad sitting near the fire at night and Mam writing in her best handwriting for Dad to sign, not with a flourish now, but with a firm hand. Then he sat in his horsehair chair and would not budge.

But the envelopes kept on coming and Dad began to get angry. Then when he had dictated a letter to Mam to say again that he had not even started the engine, everything was calm again. Sometimes weeks would go by and we imagined it was really 'the end' at last but then another brown envelope darkened our mantelpiece and cast a shadow over everything again. Now when Dad signed his reply I began to see fear in his eyes.

You see, Uncle Sid came in one morning and said he had been doing a bit of research – he was good at that sort of thing – and it turned out that the lad on a motorbike was a son of a very rich gentleman who came from down south.

"Get out of it now," said Uncle Sid. "Get out while you can – you can't fight the Big Boys, they have enough money to hire expensive lawyers – just say you're half to blame – accept fifty-fifty and that will be the end of that." Mam, Aunty Vera and even Grandma and us kids all stood round agreeing with Uncle Sid. We wanted to get back to normal and to see my dad safe again.

"I cannot tell a lie, though," said my dad and he sat down at our table and put his head in his hands and it was a long time before he looked up again and his blue eyes seemed so afraid. But then he just got up and put his cap on and went outside to get on with his work.

Next day Posty pedalled down our road with an even bigger envelope for my dad – it was heavy and cream this time and looked even more important. My dad read it when he came in at 11 o'clock for his mug of tea – Mam stood hovering and I sat on our couch and watched.

"They're taking me to court – I have to go to Hull assizes," and he put his head in his hands again for a very long time then he went next door to use the telephone and rang up to see his solicitor straight away. He got dressed up in his suit, which he only used for weddings and funerals, and he put his best trilby on and set off to Hull in our car.

But when he came back it was even worse news – his solicitor had agreed with the insurers and advised him to accept that he could have been partly at fault, but Dad was having none of that.

"I hadn't even started van's engine. How could it have been my fault?" he said. Mam was scared out of her wits and she tried again to persuade him to 'compromise' but no, he could not tell a lie, he would tell the truth.

"I'll do what it takes to prove I'm innocent, even if it means going to Hull assizes."

And that's what happened he had a final letter that told him when he had to go to court. It was awful.

Then there was even more bad news because his solicitor phoned up and said that on considering the case he now had to advise Dad to plead 'Guilty', of course Dad would not. But what if they judged him and found him guilty anyway? I thought that he could be put behind bars. But my dad would not change his mind.

"I will tell the truth. I will not tell a lie," he said but his solicitor said that it would be just his word against the motorbike lad and it now seemed that it would be better all-round if Dad pleaded guilty and he would be bound to get off lightly.

"I will tell the truth," said Dad again, he sounded brave but I could see white fear in his eyes.

When the day came, he scraped his whiskers off with trembling hands and put his collar and tie on but this time there was blood on his collar from where his razor had cut him. Mam spit on it and rubbed but it stayed bright red. Then wearing his funeral suit, he set off in our car to Hull assizes. He would not have a chance. Dad didn't have posh ways and he would not know how to win in court with all the clever lawyers and their fancy words. My dad wasn't good at that sort of thing.

We all stood watching, like we did when he and Uncle Sid set off to Scotland. I saw our car go up our lane then turn onto our main road towards Sunkstead and then it went round a corner and over the horizon out of sight. But this time it was different because in my mind I could still see Dad grasping the steering wheel with white knuckles with his pipe clamped tightly in his teeth as he stared ahead with fear in his eyes. He was going to his slaughter like our cattle at Hull market. We might not see him for a very long time.

But he came back sooner than we thought – our car raced into our yard and out jumped Dad and practically ran into our house. Mam was polishing the table – she had polished our whole house as quickly as if she was in a race. In fact, she had polished it from top to bottom since he set off and she was going over it again.

"Thrown out of court!" shouted Dad and with a flourish he produced a present for Mam from behind his back – a big bunch of flowers – we had never had any flowers in a vase before. Well to tell the truth, we didn't have a vase but Mam got a big white jug and stood them in the middle of our highly-polished table where they held their heads high in victory. She was very pleased with this present, I could tell by her smile she thought it was much better than the peeler and corer Dad bought her from Scotland. This time there were no angry words just laughs and shrieks from us kids.

News soon got out that Dad was back and everybody crowded round him and he told us what had happened. I should think that he exaggerated a bit to make it a better story but the outline of what happened was true. This is what he told us.

When he got there, the court was full of people in black suits and when the judge came in they all had to stand. And the judge sat on a platform above everybody. Then Dad had to say 'Guilty' or 'Not Guilty' and he said that he was not guilty. Then the rich lad and his lawyers from down south shook their heads – it was looking bad for my dad and there was silence in court. Then a door slammed and everybody turned round and looked and there was a chap with a red scrubbed face and a flat cap on. He whispered to the court usher and the usher went to the judge and whispered to him. Then this chap was brought to the witness box and as he passed Dad he lifted his cap and said "How d'ya do?" and Dad realised who it was. Dad stopped when he got to this part to add to the effect – and Mam put a mug of tea in his hand – he took a sip.

Who was it? we all wondered.

Well it was Ricky – the drover from market – he'd only just heard about the court case from his auctioneer, who knew about that sort of thing, and he ran and got scrubbed up and went to court as fast as he could. He was taken to the witness box and sworn in to tell the truth, the whole truth and nothing but the truth. Then he said that he had seen that young lad bump into our van, he had jerked forwards too fast when he started his bike up. He said that Dad had only just got into our van and hadn't even turned the key. Ricky had been in Aunty's café having a break when he saw it all through the window. He hadn't thought to say anything at the time because he didn't think anything would come of it. I secretly thought that Dad's luck money had done very well for him that day. Anyway, we were all very relieved I can tell you and then everybody went back to work except Dad who stayed in for a bit longer and had another mug of tea.

Of course, when he told his tale to Aunty Peggy it was different – because not only did Ricky come to court but every drover from Hull market had turned up to tell 'The truth, the whole truth and nothing but the truth' and prove that my dad was innocent.

Then he told Aunty Martha that not only did all the drovers come crowding into court but Aunty from the café came as well with a big plate of sausage and mash for the judge. Dad's tale grew and bigger and better and better.

He told his tale so many times and we laughed so much and it was one of his best party pieces for a very long time. Of course, we all knew that Dad always told the truth except when he was telling a tale when he exaggerated for effect. He could never tell a real lie like I had done to Mr Bantam. All the worry about my dad had put my sixpence to the back of my mind. Now it was at the front again and it seemed very unlucky to me not at all like Dad's half a crown.

I thought again of my miserable little lie about my pretend birthday, and Mr Bantam's sixpence was still lying there in my box and I felt even more ashamed. I began to dream about it – I was taken to court and Mr Bantam was a judge and there was no witness like Ricky to tell everybody that I was innocent – well I wasn't, was I? I was taken off and locked up behind bars because I was guilty and for some reason there was blood all over me.

My nightmare would not go away and I knew that I had to do something. I knew that it would be best to own up but I just couldn't bear the thought that Mr Bantam would know I hadn't been telling the truth. I would never get on in the world if I was known to be a liar. So one day I made a plan.

I took that sixpence out of my cracker box and took it to school with me. I had to make sure it got back to Mr Bantam without him knowing. And this is what I did. At dinner playtime, I went up to Miss Kenny who was busy turning a skipping rope for some kids. She had put her basket down near our school wall. I walked slowly past her basket pretending not to even look at it. And just when I was right next to it I carefully dropped Mr Bantam's sixpence in – it landed on her hanky without a noise and I walked on and away.

I knew Miss Kenny would find it and hand it in to Mr Bantam in case one of us kids had lost it – but of course no one would claim it and so Mr Bantam would have his sixpence back. I never told anybody about that sixpence not even to tell a tale and make everybody laugh.

I even kept quiet at school when it really was my birthday in May. But when I went out to play Mr Bantam came up to me without me even saying anything and he said, "Happy Birthday." He didn't smile but he did link up with me and at last I skipped slowly once round the playground with Mr Bantam. To tell the truth, though, it didn't feel as good as I thought it would.

Chapter 17

Gardens

I always dreamed of being allowed to go into Mr Bantam's garden that was hidden behind his house at school. You see, you only got to go in his garden if your teacher was pleased with you. You had to be very special to go in there. Everybody in our class wanted to go in except Charley, of course, he didn't care about anything. Edmund and Virginia from our class went in but I never did anything good enough to please mean Miss McBride. It would be my dream come true if I could go in that garden to hear the singing birds and the bees buzzing in and out of the bright flowers.

At our house, we never really had a garden – well we did have a garden but not like at school. For one thing, you could go in our garden anytime you wanted and it was nothing special. I used to stand on our grass path and watch while my dad dug long deep furrows of sticky clay in autumn, ready for his greens.

On one side of the path near our house Dad planted cabbages. On the other side of the path there were goose gogs. Everything that was in our garden was planted for us to eat and everything was just green or mud brown. So, you will understand that I was trying hard to think of something good I could do to please Miss McBride so I could get in Mr Bantam's garden. I needed something I could tell her that I had done or something I could show her but nothing came into my head. I stared sadly at our vegetables and then over across our path to rows and rows of sour green goose gogs. (Mam used to tell us to call them gooseberries but we never did.) We had about a hundred bushes and in summer we had loads of hairy berries and us kids had to pick them all for Mam to make pies or jam. So, there it was, goose gogs or cabbage that's all we had. There was nothing at all pretty or flowery about our garden unless Aunty Vera came in wearing one of her bright dresses that billowed in the breeze.

And sometimes she did come in to help us and she told us jokes and we all laughed while we picked. We filled pint mugs and piled our colanders high and then tiptoed through Dad's cabbage plants to get to our wash house windowsill. Then Mam pushed up our sash window and took the goose gogs to make a pie for our tea.

But one day when Mam opened our sash window as usual and reached out we heard her shout, "Oh no – I've lost my ring." Her engagement ring had fallen off her finger. I don't know how it did, it just did, us kids stopped picking and stood there staring at her as she cried out again. "Come quick. I've lost my ring." Then we all ran over to her, confident that we would soon find it. After all, it couldn't have gone far; it had just dropped down onto our mud. But however hard we looked, we couldn't see it.

Mam was very upset I can tell you – well I was upset as well because it was a beautiful ring – it had three diamonds full of light and when you looked closely you could see all bright colours that sparkled and shone and winked at you. It was as if a whole garden of bright flowers was hidden in there. I loved looking at it on Mam's hand and listening to how Dad gave it to her and how they hoped to be happy ever after. It was full of her dreams and it was very precious to her and now it was gone and our sticky brown mud had swallowed it up. But even though we were all very sad we still had to keep on picking our goose gogs. There was no time in the day for dreams of jewels and being special and hidden gardens full of bright flowers and buzzing bees and singing birds.

Of course, we had some birds of our own in our garden but they were just ordinary brown sparrows that twittered busily all day long. They made little holes in our dried-up mud so that they could wash in dusty mud baths. Then they picked up bits of hay and roots and made straggly nests in our hedge. You could easily see them. They were untidy and tumbled about all over – our sparrows didn't even bother to hide their nests which was a big mistake because we also had some other birds called magpies in our garden.

We had two big black and white magpies that swooped around and made loud cackling noises like witches on their way to their twiggy nest high up in our old conker tree. Magpies were not very nice birds because they stole shiny things, I knew that from reading my comic and it said that when they saw bright things they grabbed them and put them in their nest. Another thing that I knew was that they stole baby birds if they could find them. And of course, they could easily find baby sparrows from our twittering families. Magpies were bad news and if you saw one it was unlucky.

Our magpies used to sit in our conker tree and watch while busy little sparrows built their straggly nests. They just sat there watching and biding their time. They didn't even have to try they just had to wait. They hardly gave our baby sparrows time to roll out of their shell when they struck. With a loud cackle, they swooped down and grabbed a baby – it was still just a tiny see-through blob like our goose gogs with hairs sticking out and a little head and little tail. Their mams and dads did their best and they made a huge shouting noise and all our other sparrows joined in, but it was too late. They shouted as loud as they could but they did not scare our magpies who just did not care. All they cared about was getting something good to eat. And with a flash of black and white they were gone with their bellies full of baby sparrow.

It made me feel sick and when I went in for tea I couldn't even eat Mam's pie – I kept thinking of the little baby sparrows with little hairs on and fat round bellies and I kept on thinking that Mam had made baby sparrow pie.

That night to cheer myself up I thought about Mr Bantam's garden at school again. I really wanted to go into his garden because I was sure it would be the most wonderful in the world, even better than Sunnyside garden. I thought longingly of the gate that led from our playground and the path going past the school house into the garden and I thought of the little wooden seat that Virginia had told me about. You were allowed to sit on it and read if you were a boy or knit if you were a girl. But if I went in I would just look and listen and I would not knit which I wasn't very good at anyway.

I would be so happy listening to the singing birds and the bees would buzz in my hair like they did in Mr Grey's hair and I would watch the flowers billowing like Aunty Vera's dress. I thought about it every night before I went to sleep, it would be my dream come true. I just had to try and do something good.

But how ever hard I tried I was never good enough to go in that garden. Doreen never got to go in either because she was not good at school work but Edmund got to go in nearly every week because he was so good at sums – he was very special. He used to take his book about Robin Hood to read and he was away, out of our class, for ages while we did our sums and spelling, over and over again with mean Miss McBride. Virginia got to go in nearly as much as Edmund because she was special as well and she was so good at spelling. She took her knitting in with her and even that was special. She was knitting a lacy gown for her pretty blonde doll.

Even Brenda got to go in the garden once when she brought a bunch of bright flowers for our teacher, from her garden. Brenda was knitting a scarf for the winter and she took that with her and when she came back ages later she had knitted inches and inches. But I didn't please Miss McBride, I wasn't good enough at sums or spelling and we hadn't got any bright flowers in our garden. We only had mean green goose gogs or cabbages and I didn't think that they would please Miss McBride. It looked as if I never would get into that garden. And I bet it was because I had seen magpies, I saw one every day and they made me unlucky.

But if I thought I was unlucky in everything, I had reckoned without Aunty Vera because one day she gave me a packet of seeds. I had never had any seeds in a packet before. I could hardly believe it – we didn't usually get presents at our house unless it was your birthday or Christmas but one day Aunty Vera gave this packet of seeds to me just because she wanted to.

'Virginia Stock' I read and I looked at a picture of lovely little white, pink and purple flowers all shining out like jewels. Maybe our Virginia at school was named after them because she was so lovely and so special. 'A beautiful and very special flowering annual' I read from my seed packet and it said that they grow up to one foot high and that they are best in sunshine and that they will flower in summer. 'Sow seeds in fine tilth in spring' well, it was getting on for summer by then so I had to move quickly.

Dad gave me a patch of mud to dig next to his cabbages near our house. I dug it on a night after school, just like I had seen him do – well not as good as him because no matter how hard I jumped on our spade it just didn't go in like it did when Dad dug. But I worked on, listening to our little twittering sparrows forever dragging strands of hay and our magpies forever cackling like witches watching from their conker tree to see what they could steal.

Then in a flash, I had a sudden thought. That was it – why hadn't I thought of it before? The magpies must have stolen my mam's ring – of course they would have – they would have seen it fall and when we weren't looking they would have swooped down and picked it up and taken it to their nest. They were famous for it, everybody knew that they were thieves, and that they liked stealing shiny things, as well as baby birds. If I found Mam's ring surely Miss McBride would think I was special enough to allow me into Mr Bantam's garden. So, I set off to climb our conker tree. I was trembling with excitement and my heart was beating fast.

I soon calmed down though and concentrated on my climbing, it was easy at first – I had done this loads of times before. But our magpies' nest was right in amongst tiny branches at the very top of the tree. Up and up I went to where I had never been before until I was balanced on thin little twigs that cracked and swayed but I climbed on – it was a good job I was only a light weight.

I could hardly see their nest now because it was hidden by leaves bigger than my hand but I knew it was there because in winter you could see it high up like a big black ball. Then I heard the magpies cackling and all at once this huge witch's nest was blacking everything out. Now one final heave and I was squinting in a muddy bowl full of big mean green eggs. I put one hand in – holding tight with my other hand onto a thin branch. I felt the warm eggs but there was no sudden feel of a cold gold ring or sudden sight of bright colours of diamonds and dreams come true.

It had to be there. After all my effort, Mam's ring just had to be there – but it wasn't. No matter how many times I felt all around, there was nothing but eggs and mud.

I had one last desperate feel and then I heard a great cackle of a magpie as it shouted really loudly at me for being at her nest and I leant back and started down sadly without my prize. Now there was going to be no running to Mam to tell her what I had found and worst of all no telling my teacher and no 'Well done – you can go to Mr Bantam and he will let you into his garden'. At least I could put – climbing trees – on my 'What I am good at' list. That cheered me a bit but I knew that would not get me into the garden.

I had to keep on trying to think of something else I could do to get me into that garden. And just then I suddenly got another idea in another flash. Maybe if I got on with sowing my seeds and maybe if I got some really beautiful Virginia Stock flowers growing I could take my teacher a bunch and she would give me a 'Well done, see Mr Bantam' at last. That was it – I went back to my bit of mud and hammered my rake on it to squash every lump and then I raked it again and again till I had a 'fine tilth'. Now to get on with sowing my seeds, I ripped at my packet and out came some tiny grains. I held them in my palm and stared – I couldn't believe that these little things were going to give me a bright bunch of flowers and dreams come true but I had to try. I carefully let my seeds drizzle out of my hand and into my tilth in a row and then I put two sticks in to mark where they were. Then I covered them up with more even finer tilth and watered them in and waited.

I must say I was very surprised that I didn't have to wait very long because after only one week I could see a row of little tiny seedlings pushing up and after two weeks they were growing so fast I decided to measure them every day. One inch, two inches, three inches – they were growing well – I went every morning with Mam's inch tape and wrote my measurements on a bit of paper – I could show this to Miss McBride as well for extra praise – I might even get longer in Mr Bantam's garden for that. Our two magpies cackled over me but I didn't look up at them I didn't want them bringing me bad luck any more.

Funnily enough it wasn't our magpies that did any harm this time it was our little ordinary twittering sparrows. One hot day after school I went to water my Virginia Stock plants but they were nowhere to be seen. I couldn't believe it, where had they gone? All I could see was bits of dried up leaves and roots, flat on the ground and there were holes in my fine tilth – our little sparrows had made mud baths and flattened my row of plants – oh, how could they? I just stood there and shouted, "Oh no, how could you?" over and over again at the sparrows. Now I would have no flowers and no telling teacher how they grew and no going into Mr Bantam's garden.

"What's wrong?" that was our Katy who had heard me shouting and had come to see what was going on – I could hardly speak but anyway I didn't need to, she could see for herself as she bent down looking at my dead mud garden.

"What's this?" she shrieked suddenly.

"It's Mam's engagement ring! I've found Mam's engagement ring!" And off she ran to Mam, rubbing up her find to get a shine on the diamonds. Mam would be very pleased with our Katy. Oh, if only I had looked more carefully I might have seen that the sparrows had uncovered Mam's ring when they fluffed up their feathers to make their bath in my tilth.

If only it had been me that had found it, I would have got into Mr Bantam's garden for sure. But it wasn't me who found Mam's ring. I bent down and tried to plant my floppy little dry plants again. I watered them in but I knew it was no use – they were dead and their roots were dry like hay and they couldn't suck up water any more. Another chance for me to get into Mr Bantam's garden had gone and I was sad.

At least Mam was very happy – for one thing she had got her engagement ring back and soon it was cleaned up and on her finger, again, next to her wedding ring and it seemed to me that it sparkled even more and hundreds of colours and dreams shone out from it.

And another reason for Mam to be happy was that next week it was Ringam Carnival and she loved that sort of thing. She got busy with her sewing machine and was soon rattling up outfits for us all – us kids were going to enter the fancy dress competition and Mam was going to be part of the Women's Institute float – they would decorate a lorry and then get dressed up and ride round the village waving. That year they all had to be flower girls and Mam was making herself a bright flowery dress like Aunty Vera's and she made a Bo Peep hat and then she decorated it with flowers and filled her old shopping basket with flowers as well. They weren't real flowers of course because we hadn't got any, not even Virginia Stock thanks to our sparrows; she made her flowers out of bright scraps of material. Aunty Peggy and Aunty Martha would be on the float as well but they would have real flowers of course from Sunnyside's garden.

I was going in for our fancy-dress competition dressed as a flower girl – of course I wouldn't be on the WI float like Mam but I would go and be judged in our school playground with all our other kids who were dressed up and then we would walk from our school behind the floats as they went round Ringam in a parade. I wore my best dress that Mam had made for Edmund's party and though I say it myself I looked really good. It was my mam's soft velvety flowers that did it though – they were so big and bright – and she filled a little basket full of them for me and put one in my hair with a grip. I was bound to win. And of course, this was another chance to please my teacher and get into Mr Bantam's garden.

When I had won, I could go and tell Miss McBride and even she could not be so mean as to stop me going in the garden then. She would be so pleased with me and I would be able to go in straight away, but to be extra sure I put my lucky charm bracelet on. I had not seen or heard our magpies recently so that was good sign. I think they deserted their nest after I had felt their eggs. Serves them right for stealing baby sparrows; I hoped that I was never going to see them again.

I stood very still in front of four judges in our school playground – there were four women with big hats and coats on and one had a fox fur round her shoulders. They looked very important and very hot and frowny on this bright sunny day. It was a very serious business – a lot rested on this competition and not just for me. Everybody took it seriously. We all wanted to win, except Charley of course who didn't care. Mams all over Ringam had tried so hard to make outfits for their kids – even Edmund dressed up for the competition. But I never believed that Edmund's outfit was made by his mother – she didn't sew anyway – no, they'd got it from a shop in Hull; you could bet on it.

He strutted to our straggly line dressed in a perfect green Robin Hood outfit. He carried a pretend bow and arrow. The judges couldn't take their eyes off him and they hardly looked at us other kids. Of course, Edmund won and got a certificate and five shillings.

There was a bit of muttering about it being unfair and that you couldn't hope to compete with a shop bought outfit but nothing came of it and Edmund went forward to the judges' table and was presented with his prize and we all clapped politely. I didn't win anything.

Then up strode a photographer from the *Hull Daily Mail* and to my surprise he didn't take Edmund's photo or even one of Virginia who was on a float. Instead he went to the WI float and he didn't bother with my mam or Aunty Peggy or Aunty Martha, he got an old lady instead. He took her hand, she looked lovely in her bonnet and old long flowery dress and her basket was full of big daisies and her face was creased with smiles. Then I recognised her – it was Doreen's Grandma and I couldn't help smile myself as I watched her kindly face. Then a funny thing happened – I found myself being steered towards that old lady by the photographer and he stood me next to her. She laughed and put her hand on my shoulder.

"How lovely you look. Will you stand with me and have your photograph taken? You'll be doing me a favour as I'm very nervous," she said.

'Flash' went his camera and 'flash' again and we smiled and laughed and she hugged me. Then I watched as Aunty Vera, wearing one of her flowery dresses, crowned our Carnival Queen, and the Maid of Honour was Virginia. They stood on our first float and led our parade with all our other floats following. Us kids followed behind in our fancy dress. We walked all round Ringam and shouted and waved to everybody who had come out of their houses to see us.

The excitement died down when we got back to our school playground and all the adults started clearing up. I stood there waiting for Mam and Dad but suddenly I saw the gate to Mr Bantam's garden again – nothing unusual about that you might think, I'd seen it loads of times but this time it was open and I mean open – it was wide open. Well I just couldn't resist – I took a quick look round to see that nobody was looking then I ran down the path – it was easy – one minute I was in our playground and next minute I was in that garden of my dreams.

At first I kept hidden among bushes which grew all along one side so nobody could see me and I only peeped out every now and again. But it was quite safe, everybody was busy clearing up and they were not bothering about me so I explored everywhere – I sat on that seat and swung my legs. I sniffed at big bright flowers and listened to singing birds and chased huge bumble bees hoping they would go in my hair. I was having a great time but then suddenly I heard voices coming from down a path so, quick as a flash, I climbed an old apple tree – this tree was nowhere near as hard to climb as our conker tree so in a few seconds I was high up and covered in leafy branches.

I looked down and I saw Mr Grey come into view, there were plenty of bees here so he would love it but they didn't go in his hair this time because he was wearing his best trilby hat. And then I couldn't believe my eyes because along came Miss McBride wearing a lovely turquoise floaty dress and guess what? She went up to him and held his hand – just imagine, mean Miss McBride and gentle bumbly Mr Grey, holding hands, that could only mean one thing – they were going to get married. I just sat there on my twiggy perch hardly daring to breathe in case they saw me. But I need not have worried; they only had eyes for each other and they didn't look up but strolled off still holding hands and laughing. When I was quite sure they were out of sight I scrambled down and ran off as fast as I could, back to our playground, hoping that nobody had seen me.

But it seemed that somebody had seen me because a few days later Mr Bantam sent for me out of Miss McBride's class and I went into his office trembling and with my heart beating even faster than when I climbed our conker tree. What excuse had I for trespassing? I hadn't earned my place in his garden because I never could do anything good enough.

"You have done something no one has ever done from this school before," said Mr Bantam in his deep strict voice and I trembled even more.

"You have been in..." here it comes I have been in his garden when I haven't been good and special enough.

"You have been in the *Hull Daily Mail*, look here." And he showed me a picture of me with Doreen's kind grandma and we looked really good in our flower outfits – and Mr Bantam was smiling now.

"This is just the sort of thing that gives our school at Ringham a good reputation and we have never had anyone from here in the paper – not even me." I couldn't believe my luck

It's not a boy!

All my trying had come to nothing and now I had done something good without even knowing. I could even put – getting my photo in the *Hull Daily Mail* – on my list now, that was two things in a very short time.

"I am going to reward you – you can go in my garden for a whole hour this afternoon," beamed Mr Bantam. And so I was allowed to go in his garden and my dreams had come true – I even did a bit of loose knitting because I didn't need to spend time looking – I had seen the garden before. Of course, I didn't tell anybody that I had been in there already, not even Brenda.

But there was something I could tell people. I told them that Mr Grey and Miss McBride were going to get married and all the kids at school (except Charley) thought that I was very special indeed because the next day Miss McBride came to school wearing an engagement ring with three bright dreamy diamonds and everybody was amazed that I was the first to know about it.

Chapter 18

Across the Water

There was something I didn't tell you about when Great Aunty Dolly was dying and I had started to think about it lately. It happened when my Great Aunty Dolly from Sunnyside was waiting to die and she just couldn't, then as she sat near the fire getting colder and colder and thinner and thinner she closed her tired pale eyes and moaned, "Help me across, Dilly." And I whispered to my mam to tell me what she meant and Mam said that Dolly wanted to go to heaven and be safe but she just couldn't get across the water. She could not find a bridge or a boat and she couldn't swim – none of us could in our family. So, she cried over and over again to her dead sister, "Help me, Dilly." Of course, in the end she did die so maybe Great Aunty Dilly heard her and somehow helped her over. So, Dolly was safe across the water, but once, when I was a long way from home something awful happened to me across the water and it wasn't safe at all.

It all started with Miss McBride who was going to get married in our summer holiday and then she would be called Mrs Grey. Sometimes Charley in our class called her Mrs Grey before she was married and of course Fatty copied him to try and be one of the gang (but he never was) and all the other lads laughed. Then all us girls laughed as well and Miss McBride blushed very red. I wish that I hadn't laughed because I felt sorry for Miss McBride but I had joined in just the same. Then sometimes Charley sniggered instead of laughing but he wasn't thinking about her name this time and he kept nudging and winking with the other lads. I didn't know what could be so funny about getting married. Miss McBride didn't talk to us about the wedding because of Charley's laughing and sniggering but Mr Grey told his class that after they were married they were going to have their honeymoon holiday in Scotland because that was where Miss McBride came from.

Mam had always tried to persuade Dad to take us all away on holiday but as you know we had never been on a long holiday because Dad didn't want to leave our farm or Gum. Even when he went to Scotland to buy some sheep he couldn't wait to get back.

"East, west – home's best," he said – that was another of his sayings and so all we ever did was go out for a day on a Sunday school trip once a year without him. But then suddenly Mam persuaded him and we were going on a proper family holiday. I don't know how Mam did it, but she did and we were going to our Uncle Teddy and Aunty Gladys' house for a whole week. We were going to Norfolk and I had never been out of Yorkshire before. I couldn't wait to go but we hadn't finished at school yet and our term never seemed to end.

One thing that had already ended though was Miss McBride's meanness because just before her wedding she started to get more mild and we got to do singing and things like that with her and some afternoons we did sewing or stories all afternoon. We had never done anything like that before with mean Miss McBride.

Then one morning we heard that we were going on a nature walk with Mr Grey's class. We had never been on a nature walk with Miss McBride but Mr Grey's class was always going on them. Anyway, that day after dinner time our class went up to our school Huts with Miss Kenny keeping us safe. Then we stood in a line with Mr Grey's class. Miss McBride and Mr Grey kept on smiling at each other and us kids were larking about and having fun and nobody told us off.

We walked for miles and miles through fields. We went on and on to countryside I didn't recognise. Mr Grey and Miss McBride were walking close together and smiling at each other and they hardly seemed to notice us – we didn't do any nature study or anything like that – we just carried on larking about and kicked up dry mud and stones and we only got told off once when Charley started kicking mud in Fatty's face and he yelped.

On and on we went then all of a sudden, a funny thing happened, I saw our house – it was in the distance but it was our house alright. I was good at seeing things at a distance and I had put it on my 'What I am good at' list already. I could even see our conker tree and our woods and our little front door like a speck.

"There's our house!" I shouted, pointing, and everybody crowded round to look. You could see about four fields in front and then there was our house. Mild Miss McBride came to look as well and said what a nice house it looked and if she could have a house like that when she was married she would feel so safe and happy.

I wasn't happy now though because I was getting tired and it was getting late and if we missed our bus from school I would have to wait for the next bus or walk home on our main road and it would take me ages. Then in a flash I had a good idea.

"Can I walk over the fields to our house, Miss McBride?" I asked. "It's not far, I could easily get there before you are all back at school." Miss McBride called Mr Grey to help her decide. He smiled, put his hand on my shoulder, shaded his eyes and looked over to our house.

"I can't see that there would be any harm in you walking home – but are you sure it's your house?" he asked gently. Was I sure? Of course I was sure; I knew our house when I saw it with my very good eyes. So it was decided that I could go and I set off to walk home on my own while our two classes set off back to school. They all waved and shouted and soon they were a long way off and looked like little specks even to my good eyes.

I was soon across one field. I crossed another and then another. I kept looking at our house but funnily enough it still didn't seem to come any nearer. I rushed on and on. Then I realised that there were more than four fields – loads more in fact – I had crossed twice that and still it seemed no nearer. Too late I realised that because our land was flat, the faraway fields looked just like thin black lines in the distance but really, they were wide open spaces hiding behind each other. I was crossing field after field and never seemed to get anywhere. It was a great shock to me.

After a long time and a lot more walking though, our house did seem a bit nearer at last and I could see our front door and it wasn't a speck any more. I could see our Bottom Field, I could see Hoss Paster where Big Billy bull was buried and I could see our paddock where we kept our sheep in the winter. But then I had another shock.

Just when I had walked over one last field before I got to our own field and safety – I came across our big deep drain – and I was on wrong side. I had completely forgotten that our drain was there and I wouldn't be able to cross it. As I stood frozen on the bank staring in disbelief I could hear the long grasses whispering and sniggering all round me. I was on the wrong side and there was no way across. I knew that there was no bridge – there was no need for us to have a bridge – our land was all on one side and I had never needed to go across till now. The murky brown water sloped past me wide and deep, I couldn't swim of course and I wished that Great Aunty Dilly was there to help me like she had helped her sister.

I didn't know what to do. I glanced behind me but I knew that it was far too late to go back– I would never catch our classes up – even if I knew where to find them.

Just then I heard a train rattle over our railway line on its way to Ringam and in a flash an idea came into my head. There must be a rail bridge over our drain somewhere, for that train to get to Ringam. I ran to see if I could find it.

I was lucky and I did find it not too far away but it was very dangerous because I had to squeeze through a tight wire railway fence and I remembered what happened to Freddy Lowe and how he was squashed flat and splattered by a train. But I did put my head onto a rail like Terry showed me to listen for trains. There was no train coming. So, I crossed over our drain on the railway bridge and then ran along the rail sleepers. I crawled under another fence and I was in our field. Soon after that I was in our house.

Of course, I was very late, what with all that walking and all those fields that I hadn't known were there and then the problem of trying to cross our drain. Mam and Dad were in our cow house milking and our Katy and Gwendy had been back for ages and my tea was cold. Anyway, at least I was safe and I could settle down and look forward to my lessons tomorrow because mild Miss McBride had said that we were doing poetry and we had never done poetry with her before.

Miss McBride read us a poem called *Ferry Me Across the Water* and I listened carefully because I was thinking about our holiday. You see, Mam told me that to go on our holiday to Norfolk we had to cross over the River Humber and we had to go on a ferry and there would be a boatman. So, you can see how I took a great interest in the poem Miss McBride was reading to us. 'Ferry me across the water, do boatman do...' I was dreaming about our holiday and it seemed as if school would never end.

But of course, it did end and at last school was over and Miss McBride and Mr Grey went off to get married. And then they would go on their honeymoon holiday in Scotland.

Our family was still waiting to go on our holiday though, because Mam had to write to Uncle Teddy first and ask him how to get there. She gave the letter to Posty and we had to wait for Uncle Teddy's reply. It came quite quickly and after only a few days Posty pedalled down our lane with the letter, but we still didn't go because Mam had a lot of preparations to do.

She started to make us all sun dresses and swimming costumes, not that any of us could swim, as you know, we only paddled and splashed. Then Mam knitted herself a white, blue and yellow cardy that looked like a sea with little waves washing over the sand.

At least Dad didn't have anything new – he would wear what he always did when he went out visiting – his cavalry twills and sports jacket. If it was a wedding or a funeral, he wore his suit of course but his suit was not suitable for a holiday Mam said. Dad wasn't bothered about clothes like Mam was.

Dad was bothered about his animals though and you could tell that he didn't really want to leave them and he might as well have been wearing his funeral suit by the look on his face. Now he began his preparations and he spent hours training our farm workers so that they could look after all his stock when he was away. It was a long job and I thought we would never be ready to go on our holiday but of course one day we did.

At last our waiting was over and we all crowded into our little black car. Our Katy, Gwendy and me squashed up in the back and Mam sat next to Dad in the front. We went up our lane and turned west at our lane end and through Sunkstead and onto Hull docks. I had never been there before – we usually went into Hull on a bus with Mam to shop or to go to my hospital but never to these docks. Now we had to catch our ferry and of course like in Miss McBride's – sorry, Mrs Grey's poem, we had a boatman. Dad had to drive our car onto to a paddle steamer and then we all followed walking over a wet wooden ramp. We were going across the River Humber. I was so excited that I didn't mind if our holiday never ended and we never came back.

But our Gwendy wasn't excited – she felt so sick because we were swaying over heaving Humber water and crossing the great swelling waves to New Holland in Lincisha. (Mam said we should say Lincolnshire but Dad never said that and neither did we.)

Soon we were on the other side of the water but we were lost. Nobody in our family had ever been across the Humber before and we had to get Uncle Teddy's letter out of Mam's handbag and read what it said.

It said that we had to travel right on down south to Kings Lynn so that's what we did. Dad set our car facing the sun and he drove steadily heading due south. Our Katy and me were hungry and wanted Dad to stop so we could get our packed lunch out of the boot. But Gwendy wasn't hungry.

"I'm going to be sick," she shouted and Dad screeched to a halt so Gwendy could get out and be sick on the roadside with Mam holding her forehead how she always did. Then we got going again with Dad driving into a summer sun as fast as he could. He had his trilby hat on and he pulled his brim down to shade sunlight from his eyes. He clenched his pipe stem with his teeth and I could tell he was tense – he didn't like driving out of Yorkshire – it was not exciting for him at all.

"East, west – home's best," he said through gritted teeth. I was starving by now and kept begging Dad to stop so we could eat. But he drove on and eventually we came to Kings Lynn – we swooped under a great big railway bridge and into a place a bit like Hull with docks and shops. Dad got tenser and his pipe stem was in danger of snapping he was biting it so hard. And to make things worse there was suddenly loads of traffic.

People in cars and on hundreds of bikes rushed out in front of us. Everybody was going home from work and our sun was now west. But we were only just through Kings Lynn and lost again. So Mam got out her handbag and found Uncle Teddy's letter again.

"After King's Lynn you head south-east," she said. Dad swung our car round and we headed away from the sun.

On and on we went through little villages and winding roads. At last Dad agreed to stop in a field gateway so we could eat our mashed boiled egg sammies ('They are called sandwiches,' said Mam again as if we didn't know). We always had lumpy boiled eggs because our hens were good layers. They were a bit dry and boring but we ate them because we hadn't had anything to eat since breakfast. Even Gwendy had one and she started to look a bit better. Dad hadn't wanted to stop because he wanted to get the driving over with and I think that he had hoped that we would be there by now. We should all be sitting in Aunty Gladys' kitchen and Dad's awful journey should be over but it wasn't.

After we had eaten every last crumb of our bread and every last yellow and white lump of egg we set off again. Dad drove on and on – us kids were looking out for signposts that said 'Oady' because that was where we were going. But no signposts said that village. Mam got her letter out again and Uncle Teddy had just written that Oady was straight on and you couldn't miss it. But we did miss it and we had to turn round and head back west and then round again and head back east. We kept stopping and asking people, "Where is Oow-a-day?" We said it loud and clear so that they would understand but they just shook their heads and shrugged. We were all very tired and our Gwendy felt sick again with all this turning round. And her mashed eggs were coming back up.Now it was getting dark and Dad had to shine the car lights on to signposts so we could read them but as time went on it was too dark for even me and my very good sight to see. So one of us girls had to get out of our car and go over to the signposts to look for Oady – but there was no Oady written there.

"I want to be sick again," shouted our Gwendy and Mam got out with her and held her forehead again. Gwendy got back in looking as white as a sheet and left her egg lumps on the grass.

Then Mam had a good idea she took Uncle Teddy's letter and got out of our car when we next got near some houses and she knocked on a cottage door and showed the people there our letter. Yes, they knew Oady – it was just down there turn left and no it isn't on any signpost – nobody goes there. Well we were going there.

Mam got back in our car. "We weren't saying it properly," she said sadly. "It's not Oow-a-day they say Odi – it's our Yorkshire accent; nobody understood us." Mam was sad that we had been saying it wrong because she always tried so hard to get us to say things right and now she found that nobody understood us anyway because of our Yorkshire accent.

Well it didn't matter now to any of us because we were all so glad that in no time at all we were knocking on Uncle Teddy and Aunty Gladys' door and when they opened it they were all smiles and everybody was cheerful, even my tired Dad. Their kitchen light shone out into the dark night and the smell of a big stew cooking made our mouths water.

From then on things seemed as if they were going well. Gwendy stopped being sick and Mam loved being with her brother and Aunty Gladys and us girls loved playing with our three little cousins. They were gorgeous, there was Rosemary – the oldest, then Heather and then baby Bryony – they were all named after flowers and you could tell why – they were all so pretty.

"My little posy," Aunty Gladys said as she put her arms round them all and hugged them and they smiled shyly and nodded their little heads. Us three sisters looked after them and took them off on long walks and Aunty Gladys packed us proper picnics (not like ours at Gum when we had to go to Miss Smith's shop for a bag of crisps and sarsaparilla). In Norfolk, we had sammies with tinned salmon in them and I had never had that before because we always had lumpy mashed egg.

I loved going down the fields to their river on my own. You couldn't see the river when you were at a distance, just like at Gum the land was so flat you only saw a few fields in front of you and then the rest were just thin black lines and the water was hidden down in between them. Here in Norfolk though it was different because you could see bright triangular sails and it was as if they were just slicing though the fields. It was only when you got up to them that you could see that they belonged to boats on a river.

I often stood on the bank listening to the reeds whispering and watching the boats and I waved to the people on deck and they waved back cheerily. I also often looked across to a little house on the bank on the other side. Sometimes a man was there digging his garden and he would wave cheerily to me and I would wave back. Everybody was so friendly.

We were all having a great time except Dad. You see, he didn't know what to do all day and he looked a bit awkward in his clean cavalry twills and his sports jacket. And he wanted to go back to his dear old Gum and his animals. Mam persuaded him to drive us about a bit to take his mind off Gum and we went to the seaside and us kids wore our new swimming costumes and we paddled and made sandcastles. Then one day Mam asked Dad to take her and Gwendy and Katy into town to look round the shops. I didn't want to go so I stayed with my little flower cousins. I decided to go for a walk with Rosemary and Heather and little Bryony – they got very excited and nodded their heads and smiled a lot when they heard what we were going to do. Aunty Gladys packed one of her posh picnics for us and put it in a basket and I set off with my little posy of cousins down the field towards their river. The sky was as blue as could be but today there was only one boat going past and we stood watching its big red swishing sails flapping and turning trying to catch a breeze. We saw a woman sailing and we waved but she didn't see us. We all sat down on the bank to eat our picnic – it was lovely. Aunty Gladys had packed all sorts of things like biscuits and cake and tinned salmon sammies again.

Then we went to pick some wild flowers for Aunty Gladys to thank her for being so kind. I looked up and saw my man again across the water. He wasn't gardening, he was just watching me and this time he had his shirt off – it was a very hot day. He waved to me and I waved back and my little cousins laughed and nodded their heads and carried on picking wild flowers. We would have a lovely bunch to take back to Aunty Gladys. Then I looked up again at my friendly waving man. But this time he hadn't got any trousers on – well he had but he had dropped them to his knees and he was waving his bare body about and with my good eyesight I could see everything. 'Call it front bottom,' my mam always said but it wasn't like any front bottom that I had ever seen before. I stared, frozen to the ground in disbelief and I heard the reeds sniggering. He kept on waving his front bottom and it was like Mr Bantam's frightening cane and I was not brave enough. The man was smiling a sort of smile but it was not a real smile. He was showing all his teeth and his mouth was wide open and he was making a noise as if he had been running for a long time but he had only been standing in his garden looking at me. He moved forwards towards the water and I knew that he was coming to get me and maybe even to get my little girl cousins as well.

For some reason, it was then that I suddenly heard, in my head, Charley's loud snigger when he knew Miss Grey was getting married and I knew now that he was laughing about this. This awful thing that was going to happen was what Charley was laughing about. I had to do something.

I looked around for the lady in a boat with red flashing sails but she had gone up river and disappeared. There was nobody to help me. I was on my own.

"Quick," I shouted to my cousins. "Quick, get everything in your mam's basket and then run." They looked surprised. "Hurry, run, run."

"Why?" wailed Rosemary and they all bent their heads down and started to cry. I picked up little Bryony and pushed Heather's back to make her hurry up.

"Why?"

"It's going to rain," I shouted into a blue, blue sky that suddenly seemed dark and threatening.

'Please let there be no railway bridge and no boat and please let him not be able to swim,' I whispered in my head as I stumbled back with my three little cousins. 'Pleeease, pleeease – let us get back safely. Help me, Dilly.' I turned round only once and he was still there waving everything and still moving forwards through the water. I didn't look back again. We ran on and on through field after field – going back seemed much farther than when we had come – we seemed to run forever.

It wasn't forever of course and at last we burst into Aunty Gladys' house and she was very surprised that we had got back so soon on this lovely day and that Rosemary, Heather and Bryony were crying. Little Rosemary's flowers, clenched tight in her hand, hung on their broken stems and everything was spoilt.

"We thought it was going to rain," sobbed Rosemary. Aunty Gladys looked up through her window at a blue sky but didn't say anything and she soothed her little girls and gave them all a glass of water and soon they were smiling again. But I didn't smile. I went up to bed – I didn't feel very well all of a sudden and I was sick when Mam got back from shopping and she came to hold my forehead like she always did.

I was too scared to go down to see the river again or roam about anywhere outside. I knew I couldn't risk it and I couldn't tell anybody what had happened either because I was too frightened to explain what I had seen. I didn't know how to describe it and the words 'front bottom' were not the right words.

Something really awful had happened this time across the water. It wasn't just like when I was on the wrong side of our drain or when Gwendy was sick after crossing on the ferry and we were lost. This felt much worse and I knew now that there was something in the grown-up world that I didn't understand. I didn't like it but I couldn't do anything about it. I wanted to go home and I wanted our holiday to end.

Dad couldn't wait to get home either, because he never got used to being away from Gum, and when seven days had gone he was in our car at a very early hour and so was I. We waved and shouted our goodbyes as our car set off on its journey back and then at Kings Lynn we headed north. Our little car seemed to know its way back home as we raced through Lincisha and never took a wrong turn. Even our Gwendy was not sick and we were at our ferry in no time at all and off we went back over the Humber and headed east and towards Gum. I can tell you I was glad to be back in our house and safely in my bed that night. East, west – home's best.

When school started again I was glad that I had gone up a class so I wouldn't be with Mrs Grey now she was married. I knew now what Charley had been sniggering about and I didn't think that it was funny at all. In fact, I bet Mrs Grey didn't think it was funny either when she saw on her wedding night, what I had seen across the water.

Chapter 19

The Boulder

It was my last year at Ringam Primary School – I was going to be in Mr Bantam's class. I had to do well and I was quite scared, it was an important year because I had to pass my scholarship which was a test to see how clever I was. If I passed, then I would get into the top class at my next school at Ripsea. Mam and Dad would be proud of me at last even though I wasn't the strong boy they had always wanted.

After our holiday in Norfolk I thought that I could do it – make Mam and Dad proud I mean. It was funny but that man who pulled his trousers down did me a favour in a way. I had proved again that I could be brave, hadn't I? Well of course I had because I escaped before he got me and that reminded me that – being brave – was already on my 'What I am good at' list. If I could get away from him I was fairly sure that I could do anything now. I could be clever and pass that test.

'Anybody can do anything' was another of my dad's sayings. I just had to be brave (which I was) and remember that I was good at a lot of things and then I would be sure to be able to put that I was clever on my list. I would work hard at school and show Mr Bantam that I was clever enough to pass my scholarship.

Mam didn't know about my 'What I am good at' list, and she thought that the best way to for us girls to get on in the world was to talk properly, mix with posh people and dress smartly. She had no money to buy us smart clothes so that was why her sewing machine was always rattling at top speed whenever she had a bit of time off from farm work.

Even now Mam was busy with my school clothes for my new term so I would look smart. She had used our Gwendy's old skirt and cut it down to fit me. Then she folded the material and sewed pleats all the way round and tacked them down, with big white stitches and big white knots to keep them in place. Then she pressed them in, banging hard on our table with her hot iron. She made me a blouse from a remnant and I had some new socks and some new navy blue knickers from a shop in Hull. I would look very smart indeed.

When my big day came after the summer holidays were over, I dressed excitedly and I put on my skirt with Mam's tacking stitches still in. Then at the last minute just before I went up our lane to catch the bus Mam pulled each knot in turn and long white snaking threads came out, and my neat knife pleats concertinaed smartly and tightly round my legs as I walked. Mr Bantam was sure to be pleased.

I went confidently into my new classroom but Mr Bantam was not pleased. He didn't say anything about my new outfit at all. He didn't seem to bother whether I looked smart or not. I don't think that he even noticed. All he wanted to know was – did I know my times tables? I had hardly sat down at my desk, after carefully folding my pleats neatly under me, before he started calling out some questions.

"Eight sixes, seven fours, nine sevens." You can see he chose all the hard ones and he strutted about our classroom like the bantam cockerel that I had seen at Sunnyside. Of course, I knew most of my tables by now but when he was there glaring down at me waiting for an answer I forgot everything. I was really scared now.

I looked back longingly at Miss McBride's, sorry Mrs Grey's class. We were in a room next to hers. You could see through the glass in the wooden screen which divided the rooms. I stared at all the young kids coming into her class and I could see her smile at them and I remembered how she had gone mild when she got engaged to gentle Mr Grey. She would have noticed my pleated skirt and said how smart it looked. I just knew that she would, but of course I couldn't go back there not only because of what I thought about her wedding night but because there was no way back, my life was moving on whether I liked it or not.

Mr Bantam moved on to spellings next and already my pleats were hanging loosely and going limp. When we were in Mrs Grey's we did our spellings by writing the word down and you had time to rub it out if it looked all wrong. But now we had to work things out in our heads, Mr Bantam called it using our brain. He made us spell out loud which was hard. I was really very scared and he was going round the class shouting out spellings and my turn was getting nearer and nearer. When he got to Brenda, I would be next and I couldn't stand it any longer. I put up my sweaty hand and asked to go to the lavatory. (Mam said that we definitely had to call it lavatory and not 'lavvy' now that we were in Mr Bantam's class.) Of course, he had to let me go in case I did anything in my new pants. I got out just in time – not for the lavatory because I didn't really want to go but just in time to miss my spelling. I waited for ages outside in the sunshine and breathed in the fresh air till I was sure Mr Cocky Bantam would have finished spellings. Then I went back in.

He hadn't finished spellings. I had hardly got through the door when he shouted, "How do you spell bushel?" Well of course I had never heard of 'bushel'. I just stood there while everybody looked at me and I hung my head like my hopeless pleats limp between my legs. There was silence and Mr Bantam shouted out his question again and everybody was staring at me even more so I had to give it a stumbling try but I wasn't right and he said that I had better get on and learn how to spell and how to do all my times tables because I needed to do that to pass my scholarship to get in the top class at Ripsea School. Then I could get on in the world and better myself. So I did work hard at my tables and spelling. There was no poetry or painting and certainly no sitting out in Mr Bantam's garden on that dear little seat. It was all using our brain now and working things out in our heads. Once a week though, we had a change because our vicar came to talk to us. We didn't have to do anything, this time. We just had to sit there. We didn't even have to use our brains.

It's not a boy!

Reverend Robinson was a big fat man – even Mam couldn't call him just plump. She didn't even call him well built but she said that he was a substantial man of God. Well anyway, he was huge and he wore a big black frock with a yellow rope belt tied round his domed belly. When he spoke, his voice echoed all round our classroom even louder than Mr Bantam's when he wanted a spelling. And another difference was that when Mr Bantam spoke he looked at us, but Reverend Robinson didn't look at us at all. When he was giving his long sermon to us he stared out through our high classroom window with his voice going up and down in all the wrong places. Then he said a long prayer and then he walked out with his head held high – I don't suppose he even knew we had been there. He had his mind on higher things Mam said because he was a man of God and that made me think that maybe when he looked through our window he was looking straight into Heaven.

Mostly, Reverend Robinson preached about things I couldn't understand and I didn't bother to even listen, like I said this was one time in class when you didn't have to do anything. But one day he told us or rather he told Heaven what a bushel was and that made me sit up and take an interest for once. Here was my bushel again and this time I knew how to spell it.

Anyway, there was no question of him asking me how to spell it because as you know he didn't even look at us and so it was no good even putting my hand up. I would have to put it back down without him even noticing and everybody else in the classroom would stare at me again.

"A bushel is a bowl to measure corn and eight gallons make one bushel," he said. I knew I could remember that because eight was my lucky number, I was born on 8th May. I might get a question on bushels in my scholarship. Anyway, he was not really talking about that, he was telling us that we must not hide our light under a bushel. I carried on listening.

"No man when he hath lighted a candle putteth it in a secret place neither under a bushel but on a candlestick," he preached.

224

"Your light is what you are good at," he added still staring out of the window. Well I had loads of things on my 'What I am good at' list so I was very pleased. I was filled with hope that Mr Bantam would be impressed.

But Mr Bantam did not seem to notice what I was good at and all he wanted was us to be clever at school work. I just had to work harder to get – being clever – on my list and I thought I was getting somewhere when I had a bit of bad news.

"All the cleverest people are born in April," Mr Bantam told us one day and just by saying it he made it seem true. Of course, you might have guessed he was born in April so that counted him in with all the clever people and of course that counted me out because I was born in May. Maybe it was just an idea in his brain or maybe he just said it to serve me right for lying about my birthday that time so I could dance round with him. And that wasn't really fair because even though he gave me sixpence, I put it in Miss Kenny's basket and she would have given him it back. The important thing though was that Mr Bantam didn't think I was clever. I had to do all I could to change his mind so I could pass that test.

I just had to pass. I couldn't bear to hear Posty coming down our lane shouting the bad news – "She didn't pass, she didn't pass." If only I was born in April then Mr Bantam himself would come riding his bike from Ringam to Gum, crowing like a bantam cockerel with the dawn chorus. Cock a doodle doo – wake up everybody.

"She passed, she passed." I could imagine him laughing and flapping his arms in the air as he freewheeled down our lane as if he was flying. All our farm workers would hear it and Grandma and everybody next door would shout 'Hurray' and they would all come running from our stack yard and from the fields to say that I had done well. Aunty Vera would throw her arms round me and Mam would be so pleased that she would ask Mr Bantam in for a cup of tea and she would be so honoured to have such an important guest that she would practically curtsey. Mr Bantam would be allowed to sit in Dad's horsehair chair.

'She's passed, she's passed!'

'Hurray.'

But I was not born in April with all the clever people and it was a great worry to me.

At least at weekends I was free of worrying about my scholarship and I could do what I wanted and I could play about on our farm with our Gwendy, Terry, Stewy and little Bonny. Tables and spellings went out of my head for two whole glorious days.

On Saturdays, we sometimes went on our picnics again and we always took little Bonny now. We ran on our main road with our wellies slapping on our legs all the way. We always said that we were going on a picnic but mostly we had no food – sometimes we just filled an old bottle with some tap water and made do with that. We didn't often have any money to go to Gum shop and see Miss Smith in her pitch-black room. But we still played about and had fun and did all our usual things like going into Gum churchyard and looking at our graves and going into Gum Church to pray (I prayed that I would pass my scholarship even though I wasn't supposed to be thinking about it) and then we went onto our island to play Hide and Seek.

Then one day when we got to Gum Church, Reverend Robinson was there and he wasn't looking to Heaven that day – no, he was looking down at the ground. We went up to him and stood as near as we dared. He didn't seem to notice us but there was nothing new in that.

"There has been a robbery," he whispered and that was unusual because he was not using his big preaching voice any more

"Gum Church candlesticks have been stolen," he told the ground and he drifted off deep in thought still looking down – we were used to him looking up to Heaven but this time I thought that maybe he was looking down at Hell. Maybe he wanted the robbers, who stole his candlesticks, to go there and stay there for ever more.

Anyway, we soon lost interest because it was very boring watching Reverend Robinson and after all it was not a school day and we didn't have to be with him at weekends. So we ran off to our boulder for some more fun.

There was a massive black boulder in our field next to Gum Church. It had been there humped on the grass ever since I could remember. Aunty Vera said that it had been there since time began and that there was a tunnel underneath that led from Gum Church. Why it was there was a mystery and nobody knew anything much about it, but she said that there were dead men in the tunnel under our boulder. So, there we were with our massive boulder in our field with dead men under it. Then Terry had a plan to lift the boulder and see the men and they would be skeletons by now and they ought to have a decent burial. We all thought that it was a brilliant idea so we rolled our sleeves up and grabbed the boulder as best we could. We heaved and strained but it was no use; it just would not budge.

Then Terry had another brilliant idea and we all ran home. We searched for sticks and iron bars (which were easy to find on our farm) and then holding them, we ran back up our lane and onto the main road and back to our massive boulder. Then we pushed our sticks and bars under it as far as they would go and pressed and pressed to lever it up but it still didn't budge. Then Terry had an even better plan.

We had to get fit he said because we weren't strong enough. He worked out some exercises for us – I had least to do because I was the smallest (apart from Bonny who was too young to do anything), then Stewy had a bit more and our Gwendy had a bit more and Terry was the biggest and best so he had to do more than any of us. Terry said that running would make us stronger, so every morning when we set off for our school bus we had to run up our lane and not walk like we usually did. Gwendy and Terry had to run up and down twice while me and Stewy jumped up and down on the spot. When we got home at night it was biceps training and Terry made weights from bags of corn fastened onto branches and we had to lift them ten times, mine didn't have much corn in but Terry's were just about full bags. In fact, Terry's were so heavy that he had to use a strong metal bar to hold them. We kept that up for a few days until Terry said that we would be strong enough and so we ran off back again to our boulder.

Off came our coats and we stretched a bit and Terry told us to flex our arms to get our muscles showing. We bent down and got a grip.

"One, two, three – heave," shouted Terry and we heaved and strained till our muscles were tight but we still didn't move the boulder one inch. We tried again and again and even used Terry's iron bar, but it still would not budge. I was so disappointed and thought that we should try another day but Terry had got fed up and said that he had another idea that was nothing to do with our boulder. He said he wanted to win a race at his school sports – by now of course he was at Ripsea School and there was a lot of competition. Terry had never been good at running but he worked hard at getting even fitter and he made up all sorts of strengthening exercises for himself. Every night after school he stripped to his waist and ran round our paddock – round and round he went doing hundreds of laps. He carried on with his weight lifting as well and when his school sports day arrived he stripped to the waist and ran like the wind. Everybody was very surprised because he won first prize. His mam and dad were so proud of him. You see, it was true anybody could do anything and I still wanted to move that boulder.

Then in a flash I had a brainwave, my dad might help me – he was big and strong and fit, after all he worked at lifting and carrying food for his animals all day long every day. With his sleeves rolled up you could see his big rippling muscles – they were like full bags of corn. He wouldn't even have to train and do exercises like we had to do.

"No – I can't, I'm too busy – got to get all mucking out done today then I have to feed up and then it's milking time," he said rushing off with his mucking out fork. So there was nothing for it I just had to go back and try again on my own. I took my coat off and flexed my muscles like Terry had shown us and then I bent down and tried to lift 'one two three ...heave'. But of course, however hard I tried I could not budge that boulder – well, how could I? It wasn't really likely, was it? I sat down to get my breath back with my back to the stone and I let my useless hands dangle down to the cold and wet and hollow underneath. And then I thought I felt a bone and I thought that it felt like a twiggy hand that got entangled in my fingers. That must be a skeleton I had touched. 'Aagh' I got up and stumbled off as fast my legs could carry me through our field, onto our main road and down our lane. It was not as fast as the wind like Terry had done but it was the best I could do. I ran on till my lungs were fit to burst and then my breath started to come in sharp stabbing breaths.

I had an infection and I was off school again and I knew now for sure that we would never lift our boulder. It would stay there, for ever guarding its secret. Anyway, I had to put it out of my mind and concentrate on breathing fresh air as best I could to get me better so I could do well in my test.

When I got back to school after weeks being poorly Mr Bantam had taught the class lots more things. I even heard that Virginia, our clever girl, was having extra lessons at night after school with a special tutor that her mam and dad were paying for. Edmund was sitting a different test as well to see if he could get into an important school and then he would not need to bother to go to our Ripsea School. I bet both of them were born in April.

Then one day, ages before I had caught up with the work that they had done when I was off school, it was time for the scholarship. That dark day was on me. When I woke up that morning I felt trapped like those men in the tunnel and I knew for sure, whether I liked it or not, that there was no way back for me. I was really very scared but I just had to be brave (which I knew I could be).

It's not a boy!

Mam had ironed my pleats back in again for the big day and they looked smart. Then Mam smiled at me and told me to breathe in the fresh air to help me do well. But I had an even better idea; I took my lucky charm bracelet from my cracker box and wrapped it in my hanky and stuffed it up my sleeve – that would help me pass if all else failed. We sat in a big room made from Mrs Grey's classroom and Mr Bantam's classroom with the screen folded back like a concertina, it was a huge room now and we could all be spread out so we couldn't see each other's answers and we couldn't cheat. I couldn't even sit next to Brenda.

"Now turn over you test papers and begin," shouted Mr Bantam. And I turned the page over and began. I concentrated and tried to remember everything that I had learnt – there was no question about a bushel, but I answered all the questions that were there.

"Put your pens down." It was over. We just had to wait while Edmund and Virginia, who were monitors, collected our papers and then we all tumbled out into our playground and the sun was shining and my charm bracelet clunked in my hanky as I skipped about and breathed in fresh air and laughed. Anybody can do anything.

Things soon got back to normal again at school – even Reverend Robinson seemed to be his old self, he had got some more candlesticks for Gum Church. I heard Uncle Sid say that the insurance had paid for replacements and they had to be kept in a locked cupboard from now on. But Reverend Robinson said that their light would not be hidden when there was a service because they would always be taken out and the candles were to be lit every Sunday. Then it all got boring because he started preaching again and told us (or rather Heaven through our window) that same old thing about hiding lights under a bushel – he must have forgotten that he had told us it once before. Then after he had gone Mr Bantam who had been standing next to Reverend Robinson said that we had to all write a story called 'Hiding your light under a bushel'. This was unusual; we had never been asked anything about what Reverend Robinson said – I suppose Mr Bantam was running out of things to do with us now we had done our scholarship and we would be leaving his school that summer. Anyway, we had to get our pens out and Virginia filled our ink wells with ink. She didn't need any and neither did Edmund because they had their own fountain pens and they had their own bottles of ink. I didn't think I'd be able to write anything because I had got bored with Reverend Robinson's bushel story but I started thinking about what Aunty Vera had said and about the men under our boulder and I started to work things out in my head and I used my brain and I made up a story.

I wrote about the robbers who stole the candlesticks. There were three men and just as they had got hold of the candlesticks in the Church they heard somebody coming so they escaped into an underground tunnel. The entrance was hidden under a stone in the church floor and so they would have been safe because they carefully put the stone covering back in place behind them. They ran on down the tunnel and nobody knew where they had gone, then suddenly there was a rock fall behind them but they took no notice and hurried on and it was so dark that they lit the candles on the candlesticks to see the way out. They soon got to a massive boulder at the exit. Now, that boulder humped over the tunnel was like a bowl turned upside down. In fact, people in the village told me later that they called it the bushel boulder. Then disaster struck because no matter how hard the robbers tried they couldn't push the boulder away. They heaved and strained from below but it would not budge. There was no going back for them either because of the rock fall and so they died and their light went out. And that is where the saying 'don't hide your light under a bushel' comes from. But that was not the end of my story.

Nobody knew the men were there until one day Uncle Sid came along with his tractor and chain which he tied it round the massive boulder and with one heave he dragged it off (why didn't I think of that before?). When the villagers looked down, there was a great big hole and out of it came a great big musty smell and round it was all pale leaves trying to grow into some light. And then everybody gasped at the sight of three white skeletons and their twig fingers were wrapped round the church candlesticks.

So, in my story Reverend Robinson got the very same candlesticks back (which I thought was much better than what really happened) and he was so pleased that he asked God to forgive the robbers, which of course He did, and so at last, they were given a decent burial in Gum churchyard and did not stay in Hell after all.

I was still scratching away writing my last sentence when Edmund was told by Mr Bantam to go out and blow the playtime whistle. I couldn't believe it was playtime already and Virginia came to collect our writing books. I enjoyed doing that story but I soon forgot all about it and went running out to play with Brenda to get some more fresh air.

A week later just before home time Mr Bantam sat us all down and said that he would read us a story. We were very pleased because he didn't often do this now because as I've said he didn't know what to do with us now we were all going to Ripsea. Edmund wasn't going though because of course he had passed to go to that important school. Anyway, we all listened and I was really enjoying Mr Bantam reading to us when I thought 'just a minute – I've heard this before' and do you know I suddenly felt my light was really shining because Mr Bantam was reading my bushel story – and everybody was listening and just by him saying it out loud it seemed to be as if my Uncle Sid had really moved that boulder. And when Mr Bantam had finished it he told the class that it was my story and they clapped and Mr Bantam gave me sixpence and I wondered if it was that very same sixpence that I had given him back all that time ago. But there was more, because he said that all the cleverest people must be born in May as well as April. And just by saying it he made it seem true.

And so, I could put – being clever – on my 'What I am good at' list, at last, and that was all I wanted because if you were clever you could pass your scholarship and that was sure to happen now. Mam and Dad would be so proud of me for doing so well and there was really nothing to be scared of after all.

It's not a boy!

Chapter 20

The Road Ahead

I didn't pass of course – my scholarship I mean – well, how could I? It wasn't really likely, was it? I had so much time off school being ill, so my times tables and spellings were just not good enough and my charm bracelet just was not lucky enough this time.

So, there was no Mr Bantam on his bike riding down our lane shouting, 'She's passed.' There was just silence. Even my mam and dad didn't say anything. I think that the silence was worst of all.

Virginia passed of course – oh well yes, we all knew she would – what with her private lessons and all. She would be going straight into the top class, which was called the 'A' class, at Ripsea School, there was no doubt about it now. Her mother and father bought her a new bike and she rode it to school ringing her bell loudly and she looked good as she dashed about here and there on it.

Edmund passed as well, we all knew he would but of course it didn't matter to him because he had already passed to go to his posh school. His mother and father bought him a new bike as well, even though he had already got one not too long ago when there was all that trouble with our gang of lads. But this one was more up to date so he could ride anywhere in Ringam as fast as he wanted. Me? I was going nowhere and certainly not to the top class at Ripsea.

Sometimes I went to our lane end and stood there staring out as far as I could see towards Ringam, just in case Mr Bantam was coming with the good news on his bike. He could have forgotten to tell me I had passed. But he never came of course. It would have been easier if he or Posty had come down our lane shouting the bad news, 'She's failed, she's failed,' and then everybody, including me, would have known for sure that I had not passed and was going nowhere.

Then one day at school there was good news at last because Mr Bantam told us that there was still a chance that some more of us kids might pass. Apparently, there was a late list that sometimes came, with extra kids' names and they had passed after all. The people who marked our test might find out that they had been too strict the first time round and not enough kids had passed. So I could be on that late list. I waited and waited again at our lane end for Mr Bantam to come on his bike. He would be pedalling fast from Ringam to Gum waving the late list with my name on it.

'She's passed – she's on the late list.'

But he never came. I knew that meant I was not clever enough. I wanted to be in the top class at Ripsea but now I would not be and could never better myself and get on in the world. I had failed.

I was filled with shame and it was like a big shadow over me wrapping round everything I did – everything was spoilt now. I was not clever after all and I had better take it off my 'What I am good at' list. My lovely list that I had written in my head all my life was not interesting to anybody, nobody had ever wanted to know about it. Then one day in my last week at Ringam Primary School I was suddenly interested in my list again.

It happened when we were waiting to see what there was for us to do – as I have said Mr Bantam did not really know what to do with us now we were leaving but today was different just like the day when we had to write a story about hiding your light under a bushel.

"Now, children, there is a new headmaster at Ripsea Comprehensive School and he has asked me to get you to complete a task for him." I sat half listening, next to Brenda – we were drawing daisies on our ink wells with the hole as the middle of the flower and ink petals all round. We weren't supposed to do this and if somebody like Fatty or Charley could see us and

236

'tell', we would be told off. But I had so much shame now one more thing could not make my life darker.

"You are to introduce yourselves to the Headmaster in writing – you must write him a letter..." I filled in my daisy with blue ink with one hand and the other hand was propping my head till something made me look up and listen properly.

"You must write down all the things that you are good at. You are to let him know all the things you are good at doing at home, the Headmaster is keen to get as full and rounded a picture..." Well, when I thought about it Reverend Robinson had said that your light was all the things you were good at and you must not hide them. Here was a chance at last to get my list out in the open and tell the new headmaster all about the things that I really could do. I couldn't wait to get my bit of paper and start. Virginia and Edmund brought paper round to us all and I bent my head and dipped my pen in the inkwell and began.

Dear Headmaster at Ripsea School,

I am good at a lot of things that nobody has ever asked me about till now. But you have asked me and so I am going to tell you about these things and they are on my 'What I am good at' list and here they are –

I was very good at laughing when I was very poorly when I was little.

I got very good at understanding what my deaf and dumb Great Aunty Dilly was saying.

I was good at finding cheques for my dad.

I was good at teaching my pet lamb to do tricks.

And then I suddenly stopped and wondered if I was doing this properly; after all I hadn't got anything to laugh about now. And my Aunty Dilly was dead now and so was my lamb and the cheque that I had found was useless because it had already been cancelled at the bank. I wasn't sure now that these things counted so I put my hand up. Mr Bantam came straight over. "Yes, what seems to be the problem?"

"I'm not sure that I am doing it properly, Mr Bantam." He took my paper and began to read and I saw a quiver on his face and I thought, here we go again he doesn't really want my 'What I am good at' list. But I was relieved to see that the triangle of skin on his bald head was not flashing like it did when he was cross.

"Carry on – that is very interesting – very good indeed," he said to my surprise. I carried on writing.

I am good at being a bridesmaid even though I was not as beautiful as the bride, Ireney, because she was in love.

I am good at being brave – I had to be brave a lot of times like when I went into hospital and I was brave when I protected Helen in our playground against that Charley, although I know now that Charley had his own reasons.

I am good at painting pictures because I won first prize with my picture of Glades in our Gum Manor Competition and I remember a lonely old man who died on his own.

I am good at playing the piano and I passed my first exam.

I am good at telling the truth now – I did lie once when I said it was my birthday when it wasn't – just so I could dance round the playground with Mr Bantam. But he gave me sixpence instead and I was so worried about it and I gave it back and I felt much better after that. So now I always tell the truth just like my dad did when he had to go to Hull assizes even when everybody told him to tell a lie. In fact, I have just added – telling the truth – to my 'What I am good at' list.

I am good at climbing trees and I can't think of anything else to say about that, except that you can see a lot of things from up there that you can't see when you are on the ground.

I have good eyesight which means that I can see things that are in the distance so I am useful to my mam and dad when they are in our car and I can read signposts for them. But I have learnt that sometimes it is not always a good thing to have good eyesight because you can sometimes see things that you would much rather not, like that time in Norfolk.

I am good at remembering plays off by heart but I learnt that you must be careful and not say everybody else's lines out loud in case they think that you are showing off.

I am good at getting my photo in the *Hull Daily Mail* and not even Mr Bantam has been able to do that yet.

And so, you see, I am good at quite a lot of things and I have learnt quite a lot of things but I am not good at being clever and I have had to take it off my list because I did not pass my scholarship.

Then Mr Bantam said that we had to write 'Yours faithfully' so I did and then we had to sign our name, so I did and then our letters were collected up by Virginia and Edmund. You might have noticed that I missed out that I was good at knowing about birds and bees. I wasn't sure about this anymore especially after Charlie laughed about Miss Grey's wedding. So I didn't say anything, just to be on the safe side.

We didn't do much on our very last day at Ringam Primary School and when the time came I walked with the other bus kids down to the bus stop. I left behind my infant teacher, kind Miss Hart, gentle Mr Grey, bossy Mrs Bantam, mean then mild Miss McBride (who became Mrs Grey), cocky Mr Bantam and Miss Kenny with her lucky basket. I just got on the bus and it revved its engine and took me to our lane end. It was all over.

It was a dull summer. I still played with Brenda of course and sometimes she came to see me and sometimes I went to see her and went down her lane with Lucky Basket pulling the trap and we played all our usual games. Then two things happened that were a bit unusual.

One was that Brenda gave me a lucky horseshoe charm for my bracelet – just like that, it wasn't for my birthday or anything because as you know that is in May and it was August by then.

She said that it was so that I would remember her and Lucky Basket when we went to our new school. Well, I wouldn't forget Brenda she was my best friend. It wasn't as if we were going to be separated because she was going to Ripsea School with me.

Another different thing that happened was that my mam and dad said that I could go to Ringam Annual Dance that year. It was my first grown up dance. I had never been before, our Gwendy had been and our Katy had been of course, but I hadn't.

First though, my mam had to make all our dresses, she made a lovely green one for herself with net over it and sequins sewed on, then she made a white strapless one out of brocade for our Katy – she had a bust now which would hold her dress up, which I thought was quite exciting. Mam made our Gwendy a lovely silky dress with blue flowers on. She had a bust as well but not enough yet to hold up a whole dress, so she had straps. Then Mam made my dress, rattling away at night on her sewing machine. She made mine with the leftover scraps of green material from her own dress. She didn't need much material because I was still little and I had no sign of a bust yet. There was no net left for me though and no sequins, but it was still a very nice dress all the same. My dad didn't have anything new because when he got dressed up he always wore his suit. But Mam had to press the creases in his trousers for him. First, she tacked them in place then she ironed them with a wet cloth over the top – it hissed and steamed till there was a sharp knife edge. Maybe if she'd used a wet cloth for my skirt pleats they would have stayed in. It was a sad thing that they had just hung out. And another sad thing was that I had to wear my old, school shoes to the dance because they were all I had now. They were big and brown and looked clumsy with my new dress but Mam said that there was nothing to be done about it. At last we were all ready.

Uncle Sid was going with Aunty Vera and so he took our Gwendy and Katy in our car and Dad took me and Mam, squashed up in our new dresses, in our van. When we got to Ringam village hall it was dark and as we jumped out of our van

I noticed that our dresses looked black and didn't sparkle at all. But then we walked into the village hall and suddenly it was all bright and spotlights were going round lighting everybody up.

To my surprise the first person I recognised was Edmund Wright from our class with his mother and father. Edmund was in a black suit with a waistcoat and a bow tie at his collar – in fact he just looked like his dad only shorter (and thinner of course). Mrs Wright towered over them both and she looked so thin that I couldn't see how all her innards could fit in her. I said that she was skinny, but Mam said she was trim and Mr Wright – well you know about him he was not even plump according to my mam he was 'well built' – so well built that his trousers couldn't get round his belly and had to sit at the top of his legs leaving his big shirt and waistcoat to cover up the rest. Anyway, Mam said that he was there as the VIP and he strolled onto the stage where we used to do our school plays but you could hardly recognise it now because it was all decorated with balloons and streamers and there was a band there with all their instruments and stands.

"Ladies and Gentlemen, it is my pleasure to welcome you all here tonight on this grand occasion..." Then we all clapped and the band struck up.

Mr and Mrs Wright were first on the dance floor then Uncle Sid and Aunty Vera jumped up. Aunty Vera looked lovely in her purple dress made by my mam. They all set off on their Quickstep – forward march and round and round they went till they must have been out of breath but they didn't stop. More people joined them till all the dance floor was alive with sound and colour whirling around my head. I saw Virginia through the crowds; she was sitting on the side like me watching the dancers. Then the band stopped and the dance ended suddenly and Aunty Vera and Uncle Sid came back to their seats near us but they were only there for a second before they were back on their feet again to dance. Soon a young man came across the floor to ask our Katy to dance. She got up and blushed bright red – I hoped that she would be careful in that strapless dress or else she would be blushing even more. Our Gwendy got up to dance with her best girlfriend and they twirled around and around with her blue flowers dancing with her. I wished Brenda was there so I could dance with her but she wasn't, because as you know she didn't come to Ringam except to school and even that was over now. I just sat with my mam and dad. Dad looked deep in thought – I bet he was thinking about his animals and hoping that they were alright without him. Then once even my mam and dad got up to do a dance – I said 'even' because my dad did not like dancing but my mam did and of course she couldn't dance with anybody else because she was married to my dad. When they had finished and they had all come back to sit with me, Dad went to get us all a drink from the bar set up in a corner. He got me some lemonade and our Gwendy had a tomato juice which is more grown up. Our Katy had a sherry because she was very grown up now what with having a bust and dancing with a gentleman. I was thirsty, because even though I hadn't been dancing I can tell you that it was really hot in there, so I made a grab at my glass to get a quick sip – and I spilt a bit ('Drop' said Mam 'you cannot get a bit of liquid – it is a drop,') well anyway whatever it was it went a long way and it soaked into my green dress and made a massive wet patch at the top of my legs. I felt so ashamed and so I sat there for a long time after that, with my hands over my dark green stain so nobody could see it. Then I heard a voice near to me.

"May I have this dance?" and I looked up and it was Edmund. He smiled a bit (and this is not a drop it was a good bit of a smile) and then I smiled back and I stood up and I noticed that my stain had dried. Edmund knew all the steps of course and he tried to teach me but it was hopeless. I just could not dance – well, how would I? It wasn't likely, was it? I had never danced like that before and nobody told me you had to do the same as everybody else. You had to know the steps. Edmund had been to lessons – 'forward, one, two; side, one, two' I just couldn't get the hang of it and my big school shoes trod on his jet black shiny shoes, so many times that he started to limp. Suddenly the band stopped and the dance ended, I was relieved and I could see that Edmund was relieved as well. He took me back to my seat and next time I saw him dancing he was with Virginia who knew what to do – I expected that her mother and father had paid for dancing lessons for her as well.

I sat with my mam and dad for the rest of the time – Dad took out his pipe and started to smoke, then it was the last waltz. Mam pulled Dad up and he put his thumb in the bowl of his pipe to put it out. Then he put it in his pocket and they went off together, dancing. Then it was all over – the main lights came on and the spotlights went out and the band played 'God Save the Queen'. We all stood up and some people sang. My mam sang but my dad didn't. He just stood very upright. Then we rattled home in our van.

After that it was not long before Mam was rattling out my Ripsea school uniform on her sewing machine. She made me a navy skirt – without pleats this time, thank goodness, and a white blouse. Then she knitted me a navy cardy. Then she bought me some new things that she could not make. First there was a tie from a shop in Ripsea, I had to wear a tie like Dad did when he was dressed up in his suit, then I had new navy knickers with a little pocket in. I stuffed my bracelet in there to give it one more chance to bring me luck and now it had Brenda's new horseshoe charm, it might work wonders and help me at my new school.

My last new thing was a real leather satchel from our cobbler in Ringam. It had little hairs on the back of the strap and it smelt like our old horse Dobbin.

I had to make do with my old, school shoes of course. With a bit of care, they would last another year, said Mam, because my feet had not grown and Dad put each shoe in turn on his shoe last and hammered some metal studs in them, just to be sure that they would not wear out quickly. In no time at all I was setting off like Dobbin up our lane, except that I was going to catch our bus for Ripsea Comprehensive School.

When we got off our bus, all us new ones had to go into a great big hall and my shoes made a loud noise on the polished wooden floor because of Dad's studs. I hoped nobody would notice. Then we had to wait for our names to be called out to tell us which class to go in. First there was Class E and then there was Class D. Charley and Fatty's names were called out off they went with some other kids, grinning at us that were still left behind. Doreen was in C and Brenda was in B, she had to go with her class and we stared at each other with wide eyes for a minute and then she was gone. We were separated. I pressed my hand on my belly to try and feel the horseshoe on my bracelet in my knickers pocket but I couldn't tell which charm was which. It was all just a lump.

My name had not been called and of course when Class A names were shouted out my name was not there either because these were the ones that had passed the scholarship. Virginia was in this lot and she set off with that last group. My name had not been called.

I was left behind and I stood there and hung my head. My new leather satchel had its strap across my chest and I could smell the doomed Dobbin again. He went for slaughter. What was going to happen to me? Maybe I wasn't even good enough for an E Class. I hadn't passed my scholarship. I wasn't good enough for any class, I had nowhere to go and so I had to stay in my dark shadow and just stare at my studded shoes in shame.

There was silence, till suddenly I heard a bang and I looked up and saw some other kids still standing like me scattered out in that hall. I didn't know anybody. We stood in silence.

Then I realised that the bang was the door opening and shutting. In flew a man with a big face and sharp nose stuck out in front. I said 'flew' because he was going so fast it seemed that his feet hardly touched the floor and he was wearing a black gown that flowed out behind him like wings. He had soft soled shoes on and they made no noise on the wooden floor as he moved. His hands were behind his back and his head was pushed forwards as he stood in front of us. A tall man in a tweed suit had marched behind him and then stood to the side of him.

"Attention, chaps," shouted the tweed suit man. And the flying man stepped forward and looked round and waited a bit (I didn't think that you waited for a drop but there was so much silence you could definitely hear a pin drop). Then he spoke.

"I am Mr Sparrow, the new Headmaster of Ripsea Comprehensive School." Well, I would never have thought that he would be called Mr Sparrow – he was not a bit like one of our little twittering sparrows that built untidy nests in our hedges. Now if he was called Mr Magpie I could understand that – he was just like one of our magpies with his white shirt and dark black cloak and sticky out beak – I bet he was unlucky as well. This was the man who would have read my letter and my 'What I am good at' list, I wonder what he thought, I bet he just laughed with a loud cackle at it.

"I am from a county called Norfolk." Oh well, it was a good job I didn't tell him in my letter what I saw in Norfolk then, I would have been so embarrassed and he might even have wanted to talk to me about it, him coming from Norfolk and all. I would have been full of even more shame about seeing a man with his trousers down; anyway Mr Sparrow was still talking.

"I am new today just as you are and together we are going on a journey to success. I have decided to hand pick a group of children who show promise but have not passed for the A Class. And you are my chosen group." Well he was not unlucky after all – he was very lucky indeed for me.

"If you work hard and do well you will have your chance and in the fullness of time you could join your gifted classmates in the prestigious A Class. This has never been offered to any pupils before. You could be on the road ahead to success." He stopped and stared at us over his big black glasses.

"I know that you will not let me down. You are my chosen ones and we are on a journey together." And with that he swooped out leaving his tweed man behind.

Me? I am a chosen one? I am going somewhere at last – on a journey with Mr Sparrow. He must have liked my letter and my 'What I am good at' list after all and maybe Mr Bantam told him I had been poorly and missed a lot of school. Maybe my charm bracelet had worked its magic what with Brenda's horseshoe and all. Maybe Aunty Martha had even prayed for me. But oh, nothing mattered now except that I was on the road to success with the Ripsea Headmaster. My mam and dad would be very proud of me because I had a chance, after all, to better myself and go up in the world even though I wasn't a boy.

"Pay attention everyone your form is called 1S – you are named after The Headmaster, Mr Sparrow," said the tweed suit man. "My name is Mr Fishwick, and I am your form tutor." Then we all had to line up.

Then Mr Fishwick said, "Forward, march to your form room." And we followed him. I heard my shoes clip-clopping on the polished wooden floor like Lucky Basket.

Now I knew exactly where I was going. The sun came out and shone through the window ahead of me as I stepped with a quick march down our bright school corridor. I held my head high thinking that I had left all my shadows and shame behind.

Vicky Turrell

Vicky Turrell grew up on a farm in Yorkshire. She attended local rural schools until, at the age of 18, she left to train as a teacher. Her further education was in the sciences at college and later she gained a degree at the newly founded, Open University.

She taught in a variety of schools and was a Head teacher for 15 years. She wrote education papers and documents and published a children's book on-line.

Vicky is the Nature Correspondent for *Oswestry and Border Counties Advertizer* and writes a regular column. She is now retired and has returned to her country roots. She lives on a smallholding in Shropshire with her husband and four hens and a duck.